A level in a week

C000038491

Glenn Hawkins, Abbey Tutorial College
Series editor: Kevin Byrne

Where to find the information you need

Letts Educational
Aldine Place
London W12 8AW
Tel: 0181 740 2266
Fax: 0181 743 8451
e-mail: mail@lettsed.co.uk
website: http://www.lettsed.co.uk

Every effort has been made to trace copyright holders and obtain their permission for the use of copyright material. The authors and publishers will gladly receive information enabling them to rectify any error or omission in subsequent editions.

First published 1999

British Library Cataloguing in Publication Data
A CIP record for this book is available from the British Library.

ISBN 1 85758 931 9

Editorial, design and production by Hart McLeod, Cambridge

Printed in Great Britain by Ashford Colour Press

Letts Educational is the trading name of BPP (Letts Educational) Ltd

Motion

25 minutes

1 a) If it takes a person 900 s to complete one lap of the circuit, then calculate:
 i) Distance travelled.
 ii) Final displacement.
 iii) Average speed.
 iv) Average velocity.
 b) Calculate the acceleration of a car that increases its speed from 20 ms⁻¹ to 50 ms⁻¹ in 5 s.

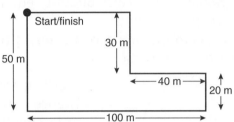

2 a) A lemming jumps from a cliff 80 m high. In the absence of air resistance, at what speed would it hit the ground? (g = 10 ms⁻²)
 b) Calculate the distance travelled by a car that accelerates uniformly from rest to 25 ms⁻¹ in 5.5 s.

3 a) The momentum of a body is the product of its _____ and _____.
 b) A cannon of mass 700 kg fires a cannon ball of mass 50 kg horizontally with a velocity of 190 ms⁻¹. Calculate the recoil velocity of the cannon.

4 a) Newton's First Law suggests that a body which has no external forces acting on it will remain _____ or continue to move in a _____ _____ with zero _____.
 b) If a footballer kicks a stationary ball with a force of 100 N, and it acquires a momentum of 5 kgms⁻¹, how long is the foot in contact with the ball?

 If you got them all right, skip to page 4

1

Motion

Improve your knowledge

35 minutes

1 You need to understand the following terms when studying motion:

- **Distance** (m): a scalar quantity equal to the total length travelled between two points.
- **Displacement** (m): a vector quantity equal to distance measured in a particular direction.

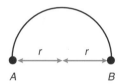

Travelling from *A* to *B*:
distance = πr
displacement = $2r$

- **Speed** (ms⁻¹): a scalar quantity equal to the rate of change of distance.
- **Velocity** (ms⁻¹): a vector quantity equal to the rate of change of displacement. Between *A* and *B*, speed may be constant, where

$$\textbf{speed} = \frac{\textbf{distance}}{\textbf{time}} = \frac{\pi r}{t}$$

whereas velocity will change because direction changes:

$$\textbf{velocity} = \frac{\textbf{displacement}}{\textbf{time}} = \frac{2r}{t}$$

- **Acceleration** (ms⁻²): a vector quantity equal to the rate of change of velocity

$$\textbf{acceleration} = \frac{\textbf{final velocity – initial velocity}}{\textbf{time for change}}$$

2 The **equations of motion** are used to solve problems concerning bodies with a constant acceleration:

$v = u + at$ where u = initial velocity (ms⁻¹)
$v^2 = u^2 + 2as$ v = final velocity (ms⁻¹)
$s = ut + \frac{1}{2}at^2$ a = acceleration (ms⁻²)
              s = displacement (m)
              t = time (s).

3 **Momentum** is defined as the product of a body's mass and velocity:

Momentum = mass × velocity

- Momentum is a vector quantity with the units kgms^{-1} or Ns.
- Momentum is important as it is related to force (see later) and is **conserved**. The **Principle of Conservation of Momentum** states that if no resultant external forces act upon a system of interacting bodies, then the momentum is constant: i.e.

momentum before collision = momentum after

$$m_1u_1 + m_2u_2 = (m_1 + m_2)v$$

Before collision   After

momentum before spring release = momentum after

$$0 = m_1v_1 + m_2v_2$$

$$m_1v_1 = -m_2v_2$$

 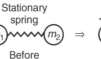

Before   After

The minus sign indicates opposite directions.

4 **Newton's Laws of Motion** state:

- I   If no external resultant forces act upon a body, it will either remain stationary or continue to travel in a straight line with constant velocity.

  Examples: a hovering helicopter or a parachutist falling at terminal velocity.

- II The rate of change of momentum of a body is equal to the force acting on the body, in the direction of that force.

$$\text{Force} = \frac{\text{change in momentum}}{\text{time taken}} = \frac{\text{final} - \text{initial momentum}}{\text{time taken}}$$

  This leads to: $F = ma$ for constant mass

- III If a body A exerts a force on body B, then body B exerts an equal and opposite force on body A.

Although the forces are equal and opposite, they do not cancel out as they act upon different bodies

Earth pulls skydiver downward

Skydiver pulls earth upwards

Car pushes road backward = Road pushes car forwards

Now learn how to use your knowledge

Motion

Use your knowledge

30 minutes

Hints

1 During a game of squash, a ball takes 1.7 s to travel from player *A* to player *B*, along the path shown in the diagram.

a) Calculate:
  i) The total distance that the ball travels.
  ii) The final displacement.
  iii) The average speed.
  iv) The average velocity.

Ignore vertical motion

The initial and final velocities are in opposite directions.
$v = -u$. *So change in velocity =* $v - (-u)$

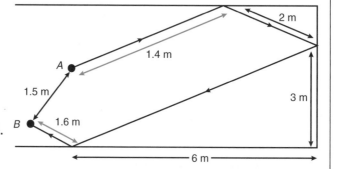

b) The ball hits a racquet with a speed 8 ms⁻¹ and leaves in the opposite direction at 14 ms⁻¹. Calculate the acceleration of the ball if it is in contact with the racquet for 0.06 s.

2 A ball of mass 0.8 kg is thrown into the air, directly upwards, with an initial velocity of 7 ms⁻¹ and is caught 1.4 s later. Determine:

a) The velocity of the ball when caught.
b) The acceleration of the ball.
c) The total distance travelled.

3 A stationary spacecraft in outer space fires a missile forwards. This causes the spacecraft to move in the opposite direction, travelling 67.5 m in 9 s. If the missile has a mass *m*, and the spacecraft 100 *m*, calculate the speed at which the missile is fired.

The final combined momenta must equal the initial momentum (zero)

4 Referring to each of Newton's three laws, explain how a helicopter hovers.

The helicopter remains airborne because there is an upward force exerted upon it by the air. Consider why this occurs

✓ Answers on page 73

Vectors

Test your knowledge

1 a) To describe a vector quantity fully, both _____ and _____
are required. For a _____ quantity only _____ needs to be
stated.

   b) Group the following as vector and scalar quantities:

   momentum, potential energy, temperature, velocity,
   displacement, distance, kinetic energy.

2 Determine the resultants of the forces shown in the diagrams.

a) 8 N →   20 N →   b) 10 N →   ← 14 N   c)

3 Determine the resultant of the two
forces shown in the diagram.

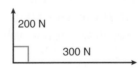

4 Determine the resultant of the two
forces shown in the diagram.

5 Determine the horizontal and
vertical components of the 10 N
force.

 If you got them all right, skip to page 8

Vectors

Improve your knowledge

1 A **vector quantity** is fully described by stating both its **magnitude** and **direction**.

Scalar quantities are fully described by **magnitude** alone.

- Examples of vector quantities: velocity, displacement and momentum.
- Examples of scalar quantities: speed, distance and energy.

2 The **resultant** of a number of vectors is the single vector that has the same result as the individual vectors combined.

- Adding vectors gives the resultant vector; i.e. if two forces act along the same line:

$$\xrightarrow{\text{10 N}} \ + \ \xrightarrow{\text{3 N}} \ \Rightarrow \ \xrightarrow{R = 13\text{ N}}$$

3 To add two vectors that are perpendicular to each other, such as two forces, the forces are drawn as the adjacent sides of a rectangle. The diagonal shown is the resultant force, where by Pythagoras' theorem:

$$R^2 = F_1^2 + F_2^2$$
$$\tan x = \frac{F_1}{F_2}$$

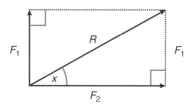

- If $F_1 = 10$ N and $F_2 = 16$ N:
  $R^2 = 10^2 + 16^2 \quad R = 18.9$ N
  $\tan x = 10/16 \quad x = 32°$

Resultant force = 18.9 N, 32° above the 16 N force to the right.

4 If the two vectors are not perpendicular the vectors are drawn as adjacent sides of a parallelogram. The resultant is found using the cosine rule:

$$R^2 = F_1^2 + F_2^2 - 2\,F_1 F_2 \cos x$$

- Angle y is found using the sine rule:

$$\frac{\sin y}{F_1} = \frac{\sin x}{R}$$

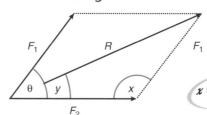

$x = 180 - \theta$

- If F_1 = 10 N and F_2 = 16 N and θ = 70°:

$$R^2 = 10^2 + 16^2 - 2 \times 10 \times 16\cos110, \text{ so } R = 21.6 \text{ N}$$

$$\frac{\sin y}{10} = \frac{\sin 100}{21.6} \quad y = 25.8°.$$

The resultant force = 21.6N, 25.8° above the 16 N force to the right.

5 All vectors can be thought of as being the result of two **component vectors**, as shown in the diagram.

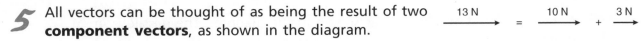

Often problems involve the identification of components that are perpendicular to each other. The horizontal and vertical components of the vector shown in the diagram are established as follows:

- Lines are drawn horizontally and vertically from the start of the vector.
- Further lines are then drawn from the end of the vector to meet the direction lines at 90°.
- Using simple trigonometry:

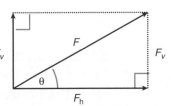

$$\sin\theta = \frac{F_v}{F} \qquad \cos\theta = \frac{F_h}{F}$$

$$F_v = F\sin\theta \qquad F_h = F\cos\theta$$

Fh = horizontal component
Fv = vertical component

- To find the component of the 1000 N force that acts along the line AB.

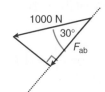

The method is the same as above. A line is drawn from the end of the vector to meet the direction line at 90°:

$$\cos 30° = \frac{F_{ab}}{1000}$$

$$F_{ab} = 1000 \cos 30°$$
$$= 866 \text{ N}.$$

Vectors

Use your knowledge

35 minutes

Hints

1 A missile is fired at 300 ms^{-1}, as shown in the diagram. The missile is in flight for 39 s.

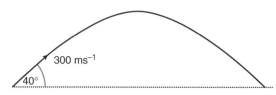

300 ms^{-1}

40°

a) Calculate the initial vertical component of the missile's velocity.
b) Calculate the initial horizontal component of the missile's velocity.
c) If the horizontal velocity component is constant throughout the flight, determine the maximum displacement achieved by the missile.

$V_v = V\sin\theta$

$s = vt$

2 Two men pull on ropes connected to a metal ring, as shown in the diagram. Determine:

a) The magnitude of a third force that would ensure the ring was stationary.
b) The direction of the third force.

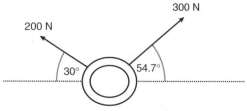

300 N

200 N

30°

54.7°

Magnitude of third force equals resultant of the two forces

Direction of third force is opposite to the resultant of the other two forces

3 R is the resultant of F_1 and F_2. If $R = 250$ N and $F_1 = 100$ N then determine:

a) The magnitude of F_2.

b) The angle between F_1 and F_2.

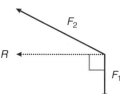

F_2

R

F_1

Construct a parallelogram

Look for the right-angled triangle and use Pythagoras

Answers on page 73

Forces

Test your knowledge

30 minutes

1 Force is a _____ quantity. It has the unit _____. A resultant force can cause an object to change its _____ , i.e. it _____.

2 A ball of mass 1.2 kg falls towards the Earth under the action of gravity. If it has an acceleration of 6.5 ms⁻², determine the magnitude and direction of the air resistance acting on the ball.

$g = 9.8 \ ms^{-2}$

3 If the system of forces shown in the diagram is in equilibrium, determine the magnitude of F.

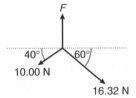

4 Determine the magnitude and direction of the turning forces about 0 produced in the diagrams.

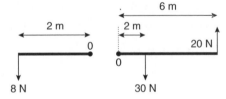

5 Determine the magnitude and direction of the couple produced.

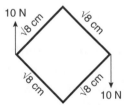

6 If the see-saw is in equilibrium, determine the mass, m.

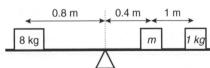

Answers

Answers 1 Vector/newton/speed/accelerates **2** 3.96 N upwards **3** 20.56 N **4** 16 Nm anti-clockwise 60 Nm anti-clockwise **5** 40 Nm clockwise **6** 12.5 kg

If you got them all right, skip to page 12

9

Forces

Improve your knowledge

1   A **force** is a **vector** quantity and has the unit newton (N). Forces can be considered as **pushes** or **pulls**. Forces can cause objects to accelerate, decelerate, rotate, change direction, change shape, change size, or break.

$$F = force \ N$$
$$m = mass \ kg$$
$$a = acceleration \ ms^{-2}$$

2   If a **resultant force** acts upon a body it will change its speed, i.e. it will **accelerate** (or decelerate) where:

$$F = ma$$

- To determine the resultant force acting on a body which is part of a system of bodies, it often helps to draw a **situation diagram** followed by a **free-body diagram**.

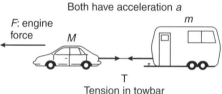

- A free-body diagram is a simplified diagram which illustrates the forces acting on one particular body:

     Car: resultant force = $F - T$

So: $F - T = Ma$

     Caravan: resultant force = T

So: $T = ma$

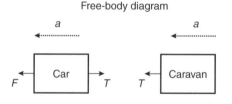

3   If a body remains stationary, or moves with a fixed velocity, under the action of a number of forces, then no resultant force acts upon the body, i.e. the forces 'cancel each other'. Such a body is said to be in **equilibrium**. One of the **conditions** for equilibrium is that **no resultant force** acts upon the body, in **any direction**.

- If the supporting string holds the mass stationary, the system must be in equilibrium. The vertical components of the tension in the strings, must equal the weight of the body.

$T\cos\theta + T\cos\theta = mg$
$2\,T\cos\theta = mg$

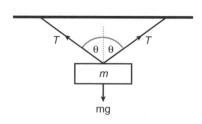

4 Application of a force may cause a body to rotate. This **turning force** is called a **moment** or **torque**.

- The size of the moment depends on both the size of the force and the perpendicular separation between its point of application and the turning point (pivot/fulcrum):

    $T = F \times d$ (anti-clockwise here)

    where T = torque or moment (Nm)

    > F = force (N)
    > d = distance between force and pivot (m)

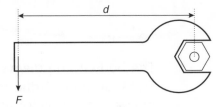

5 **Two forces** produce a **couple** if they act in **opposite directions** with **equal magnitudes**, causing an object to rotate.

- In turning a steering wheel:
  total turning force (couple)

    $= F \times d/2 + F \times d/2$
    $= Fd$ (anti-clockwise here)

    where d = perpendicular separation of forces.

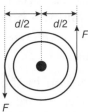

6 A **second condition** to be satisfied for a body to be in **equilibrium** is that there should be **no resultant turning force about any axis**. The **Principle of Moments** states:

If a body is in equilibrium, the total clockwise moment about any axis is equal to the total anti-clockwise moment about that axis.

- So in the diagram:

    Anti-clockwise moment

    $= 600 \times 1$
    $= 600$ Nm

    Clockwise moment

    $= 2 \times 200 + 4 \times 50$
    $= 600$ Nm

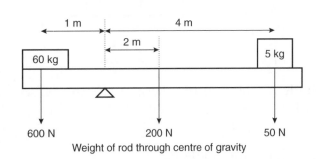

The clockwise moment = anticlockwise moment, so the system is in equilibrium (balances).

Forces

Use your knowledge

1 The body in the diagram has a weight of 800 N and is stationary due to the frictional force between the surface and the box. Determine the magnitude of this frictional force.

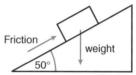

2 If the resistive forces acting on the skier and the boat are 80 N and 200 N respectively, determine:

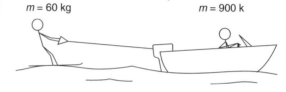

a) The tension in the rope.
b) The driving force of the speed-boat engine.

3 The system shown in the diagram is in equilibrium and the maximum tension that the supporting string can withstand before snapping is 100 N. Determine the maximum possible value of the ratio d_2/d_1.

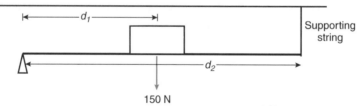

4 The body p shown in the diagram, has a mass of 2 kg and travels to the left with a steady speed of 6 ms⁻¹.

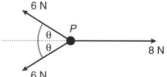

a) Determine the angle θ.
b) If the body is to accelerate towards the left at 5 ms⁻², with the 8 N force and θ unchanged, determine the magnitude of the other pair of forces if they are to have magnitudes equal to each other.

Answers on page 73

12

Work, energy and power

1 a) 600 J of work is done moving a body 8 m along a frictionless horizontal surface. Determine the resultant force acting on the body during its movement.

b) A force of 1000 N acts upon a body and causes it to move 500 m. If the work done on the body is 30 kJ then determine the angle between the force and the direction of the motion.

Electron mass
$= 9 \times 10^{-31}$ kg
$c = 3 \times 10^8$ ms^{-1}

2 a) A β-particle can have a velocity up to 98 % the speed of light. Calculate the kinetic energy of the fastest β-particle.

b) A crate of mass 60 kg is lifted onto a shelf 3 m high. Calculate the potential energy gained by the crate.

$g = 10$ ms^{-2}

3 A ball of mass 0.6 kg is thrown directly upwards with an initial velocity of 15 ms^{-1}. Determine:

a) Its initial KE.
b) Maximum height.

$g = 10$ ms^{-2}

4 A child of mass 35 kg runs up a flight of twenty stairs in 1.8 s. Each stair has a vertical rise of 0.15 m. Determine the average power developed by the child.

$g = 10$ ms^{-2}

5 Using a double pulley system to lift an 80 kg load, a pulling force of 420 N is moved through 20 m in order to lift an 80 kg mass through 10 m. Calculate:

$g = 10$ ms^{-2}

a) The work done by the person pulling the rope.
b) The useful work done on the mass.
c) The efficiency of the system.

Answers

 If you got them all right, skip to page 16

Answers 1 a) 75 N b) 86.6° **2** a) 3.9 × 10^{-14} J b) 1800 J **3** a) 67.5 J b) 11.3 m **4** 583 W **5** a) 8400 J b) 800 J c) 9.5 %

13

Improve your knowledge

1 If a body has **energy** it has the **potential to do work**. Doing work could be lifting a box, pushing a car, or a light bulb converting electrical energy into light energy. The more energy a body has, the more work it can potentially do. Both work and energy have the unit **joules** (J).

- If doing work involves the movement of a force then:

  $W = Fs$ where W = work (J)
  F = force (N)
  s = distance moved in direction of force (m).

- If the movement is in a direction other than that in which the force is applied then:

  $W = Fs \cos\theta$

Direction of motion

Work is often defined as **the amount of energy converted from one type to another**.

2 Different energy types can be broadly categorised into two main groups: **kinetic energy** and **potential energy**

- **Kinetic energy** is the energy a body possesses by **virtue of its motion**. The faster the body moves the greater its KE.

  $KE = \frac{1}{2}mv^2$ where m = mass of body (kg)
  v = speed (ms^{-1})

- **Potential energy** is energy that is **stored** in some manner. Often this is energy that is possessed by **virtue of configuration or position**, i.e. the energy stored in a stretched spring or the energy a body has due to its position in a gravitational field, called **gravitational potential energy**.

  $GPE = mgh$ where m = mass of body (kg)
  g = acceleration due to gravity (ms^{-2})
  h = height (m) above a zero GPE reference point.

3 **The Principle of Conservation of Energy** states:

In an isolated system (i.e. the Universe) the total amount of energy does not change.

This statement implies that energy **can neither be created nor destroyed**. It can however, be converted from one type to another.

- If a system consists of bodies with KE and PE, and no mechanism by which these can gain other forms of energy, then there will be an interchange of PE and KE, but the total energy will remain constant:

$$KE + PE = \text{constant}$$
$$\tfrac{1}{2}\,mv^2 + mgh = \text{constant}$$

- If a mass fell towards Earth under the influence of gravity alone, then all of the PE it had at height h would be converted to KE at the Earth's surface:

$$\tfrac{1}{2}\,mv^2 = mgh$$
$$v = \sqrt{2gh}$$

4 The rate at which work is done, i.e. the rate at which energy is converted from one form to another is known as **power**.

$$\text{Power} = \frac{\text{work done}}{\text{time taken}} = \frac{\text{energy converted}}{\text{time taken}}$$

So: $P = \dfrac{Fs}{t}$ but $\dfrac{s}{t} = \text{speed } (v)$ $\rightarrow P = Fv$

Power has the units Joules per second (Js^{-1}) or watts (W).

5 Whilst energy cannot be destroyed, it can be converted into forms of energy which are not useful. Machines and engines often 'lose' energy as heat and sound, due to friction between moving parts. A machine which 'loses' a large fraction of its input energy, is said to have a low efficiency, where

$$\text{Efficiency \%} = \frac{\text{useful energy out}}{\text{total energy in}} \times 100$$

or

$$\text{Efficiency \%} = \frac{\text{useful power out}}{\text{total power in}} \times 100$$

Work, energy and power

Use your knowledge

Hints

1 A cyclist approaches a slope with a speed of 7 ms⁻¹. At the base of the slope the cyclist stops pedalling and freewheels up the slope. Calculate the distance s travelled up the slope if the percentage resistive energy losses are:

a) 0 %
b) 50 %
c) 70 %

$g = 10\ ms^{-2}$

KE bottom = PE top

2 Consider a 'perfect' pendulum swinging in the absence of friction or any other mechanism that could result in energy losses. If at the lowest point of its swing it has a speed of 10 ms⁻¹, how much higher would it be at the top of its swing?

$g = 10\ ms^{-2}$

3 A conveyor belt lifts 300 kg of sand through a height of 10 m, in 15 s. Calculate the power supplied to the motor if the system is:

a) 100 % efficient.
b) 24 % efficient.
c) 50 % efficient.

$g = 10\ ms^{-2}$

$W = mgh$
$P = \frac{w}{t}$

4 a) The engine of a car travelling at a steady speed of 72 kmh⁻¹, on a level road, operates at 100 kW. Determine the magnitude of the forces that resist this motion.

b) If the car had a mass of 900 kg and were to drive up a slope inclined at 30° to the horizontal, how much extra power would the engine have to develop to maintain the car's speed at 72 kmh⁻¹?

Rearrange:
$P = Fv$

Extra power = PE gained each second, so find height gained each second

✓ Answers on page 73

Circular motion

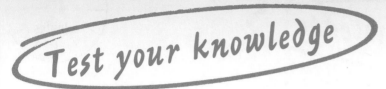

25 minutes

1
a) If $r = 7$ cm, and $s = 21$ cm determine θ in radians.
b) If θ is increased to π radians determine s.

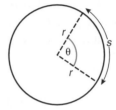

2 A particle moves along a circular path at a steady speed. If the line joining the particle to the centre of the circle sweeps out 9 rad in 300 s and the circle has a diameter of 20 cm, then calculate:

a) The angular speed.
b) The time for one revolution.
c) The linear speed of the body.

3 A body of mass 50 kg makes circular motion in a horizontal plane, with a radius of 2 m. The period of the rotation is 3 s.

a) What is the name of the resultant force acting on the body?
b) In which direction does this force act?
c) Calculate the magnitude of this force.

4 A stone tied to a string is swung in horizontal circles at a steady speed. The string has a length of 0.80 m and the angular speed of the rotation is 3.0 rad s^{-1}. If the maximum tension that the string can withstand before breaking is 14.4 N, calculate the maximum mass of stone that can be swung at this speed.

5 How much extra tension would the string in Question 4 have to withstand if the stone were to make vertical circles at this speed? ($g = 10$ ms^{-2})

Answers

If you got them all right, skip to page 20

Circular motion

30 minutes

1 If the body in the diagram moves along an arc of a circle between points A and B, then the angle that the radius sweeps out at the centre, θ, is called the **angular displacement**.

- By definition:

  $\theta = \dfrac{s}{r}$ where θ is measured in radians

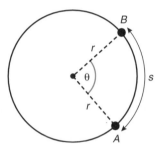

- If one whole circle is completed then:

  $\theta = \dfrac{2\pi r}{r} = 2\pi$

- Remember: $360° = 2\pi$ radians

2 If the body in the above example had moved from A to B in t seconds, then we can calculate the **angular displacement per second**. This is known as the **angular speed**, measured in radians per second, and is given by:

$$\omega = \frac{\theta}{t}$$

- The angular speed is related to the time for one revolution:

$$\omega = \frac{2\pi}{T}$$

and to the linear velocity of the body:

$$v = r\omega$$

3 For a body to move in a circle a resultant force must act upon that body towards the centre of the circle. This force is called the **centripetal force**. This unbalanced force must result in an acceleration towards the centre of the circle, called **centripetal acceleration**, where:

$$a = \omega^2 r \qquad F = m\omega^2 r$$

- Also: $a = \dfrac{v^2}{r}$, $F = \dfrac{mv^2}{r}$

4 If an object, such as a mass on a string, is forced to make **horizontal circular motion**, the tension in the string would provide the required centripetal force:

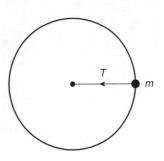

$$T = m\omega^2 r$$

- If the mass moves at a **steady speed** then the **tension** in the string is the **same** at all points of the motion.

5 If the body in the above example is forced to make **vertical circles**, the **tension** in the string **varies** with the position of the mass.

- At the **top** of the circle:

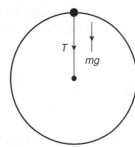

$$T + mg = m\omega^2 r$$
$$T = m\omega^2 r - mg$$

- At the **bottom** of the circle:

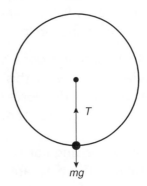

$$T - mg = m\omega^2 r$$
$$T = m\omega^2 r + mg$$

Circular motion

Use your knowledge

Hints

1 The 0.5 kg mass in the diagram is tied to a rope and makes circular motion in the vertical plane at a steady speed. The period of rotation is 1.4 s and the rope is 0.8 m long. The stone is shown in two positions, the top and bottom of the rotation where the string has corresponding tensions, T_1 and T_2. ($g = 10$ ms^{-2})

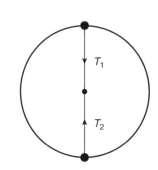

At top:
$T = m\omega^2 r - mg$
At bottom:
$T = m\omega^2 r + mg$

Determine the ratio $\dfrac{T_1}{T_2}$

2 A car travels around a circular track at a steady speed of 15 ms^{-1}. The mass of the car is 950 kg and the distance from the centre of the track to the centre of the circle is 20 m.

a) In which direction does the resultant force on the car always act?
b) Calculate the size of this force.
c) What provides this force?
d) Calculate the corresponding acceleration.

$F = m\omega^2 r$

3 a) Calculate the angular speed of the man in the diagram.
b) Calculate his linear speed.
c) Calculate his acceleration due to the Earth's rotation.
d) How does the acceleration for a geostationary satellite, one Earth's radius above the surface of the Earth, compare to your answer for part c)?

1 rotation = 24 hours

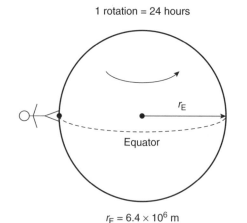

r_E

Equator

$r_E = 6.4 \times 10^6$ m

$\omega = \dfrac{2\pi}{T}$

T in seconds
$v = r_E \omega$
$a = \dfrac{v^2}{r}$

Answers on page 73

Simple harmonic motion

30 minutes

Test your knowledge

1 The mass and spring arrangement shown in the diagram oscillates between A and B about equilibrium point O. The mass takes 0.6 s to move from O to B and back to O. Determine:

   a) The amplitude of the motion.
   b) The period.
   c) The frequency.

2 A mass tied to a string swings back and forth as a pendulum. The amplitude of the motion is 5 cm and the period 1.2 s. Calculate:

   a) The maximum acceleration of the mass.
   b) The maximum speed of the mass.
   c) The speed of the mass at a displacement of 2 cm.
   d) The speed of the mass after 0.8 s. ($t = 0$ at centre of oscillation)

3 A body performs SHM with a period T. If timing starts at equilibrium, then in terms of T, state the next three times when:

   a) Acceleration is maximum.
   b) Velocity is minimum.

4 If a pendulum has a bob mass 0.8 kg and length 1.2 m, determine the period of the motion. ($g = 10$ ms^{-2})

5 A child on a swing rises through a height of 0.5 m. Ignoring resistive energy losses calculate the maximum speed of the child. (The child makes no movement to increase or decrease the swing height.)
   ($g = 10$ ms^{-2})

Answers

✓ *If you got them all right, skip to page 24*

Simple harmonic motion

30 minutes

1 An **oscillating** or **vibrating** body is one that performs a **repetitive to and fro** motion about a fixed point (equilibrium position).

- One **cycle** of the motion is from one extreme of the motion to the other and back again.
- The **amplitude** of the oscillation is the **maximum displacement** from the equilibrium position.
- The **frequency** of the oscillation (f) is the number of **complete cycles** performed **every second**.

  Measured in Hertz (Hz)

- The **period** of the oscillation (T) is the **time for one complete cycle**.
- Period and frequency are related by:

$$f = \frac{1}{T}$$

2 Most commonly, oscillating bodies perform **simple harmonic motion (SHM)**. A body performs SHM if it makes a **repetitive oscillatory motion** about a **fixed point** where its **acceleration** is **proportional** to the **displacement** from that point and is always **directed towards** that point.

- This statement is expressed mathematically as:

  $a \propto -x$ where x = displacement (m)

  $a = -kx$ a = acceleration (ms^{-2})

  k = constant of proportionality = ω^2

  Minus sign is a consequence of the acceleration always being towards a fixed point

- The velocity of a body performing SHM can be determined at any instant:

  $\pm\, v = \omega\sqrt{r^2 - x^2}$ where r = amplitude (m)

  $$\omega = 2\pi f$$

  $$\omega = \frac{2\pi}{T}$$

  $\pm$ signs indicate that velocity can be in either direction

- This leads to:

  $$x = r\cos\omega t$$

22

This equation assumes that timing starts at one extreme of the oscillation.

If timing starts at centre of oscillation, $x = r\sin\omega t$

3 The variation of acceleration, velocity and displacement with time can be represented graphically:

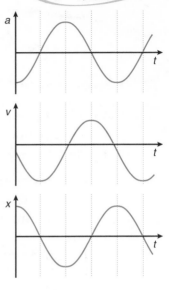

4 Two examples of bodies in SHM are a mass performing vertical oscillations on a spring and a simple pendulum.

Assumes spring has negligible mass. Otherwise use $M + M_s$ where M_s = effective mass of spring

- For the spring: $T = 2\pi\sqrt{\dfrac{M}{k}}$ T = period (s)
  M = mass (kg)
  k = spring constant (Nm⁻¹).

- For the pendulum: $T = 2\pi\sqrt{\dfrac{l}{g}}$ l = pivot to centre of mass length (m).

5 When a body oscillates there is a **continual interchange of kinetic energy and potential energy**. For a simple pendulum:

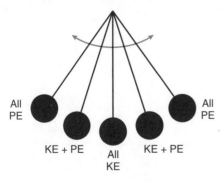

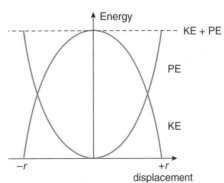

Now learn how to use your knowledge

Simple harmonic motion

30 minutes

Hints

1 A body of mass 20 kg moves with simple harmonic motion in a straight line. The period of the motion is 2 s and the maximum force exerted on the particle is 5000 N. Calculate:

a) The maximum acceleration of the particle.
b) The amplitude of the oscillation.
c) The maximum speed of the particle.
d) The maximum potential energy of the particle.
e) The speed of the particle 1.3 s after leaving the equilibrium position.

$F = ma$

$Max\ PE = max\ KE$

2 A mass of 0.5 kg hangs from a vertical spring of spring constant k. The period of the oscillation is T and the amplitude 10 cm.

a) Determine in terms of k:
    i)   The maximum velocity.
    ii) The maximum acceleration.
    iii) The velocity at a displacement of 4 cm.
b) If the spring were replaced with one of spring constant $2k$ and all other factors remained unchanged then calculate the following ratios:

    i) Max velocity$_{New\ spring}$/max velocity$_{Old\ spring}$

    ii) Max acceleration$_{New\ spring}$/max acceleration$_{Old\ spring}$

$T = 2\pi\sqrt{\dfrac{m}{k}}$

$\omega = \dfrac{2\pi}{T}$

$v = r\omega$

$v \propto \omega \propto \sqrt{k}$

$\therefore 2k \Rightarrow \sqrt{2}v$

$a \propto \omega^2 \propto k$

$\therefore 2k \Rightarrow 2a$

✓ Answers on page 73

24

DC circuits

30 minutes

Test your knowledge

1 A DC supply of 10 V, is placed across the ends of a wire conductor causing 500 C of charge flow past a point in the wire, in 1000 s.

a) Calculate the resistance of the wire.
b) If R is doubled, what effect would this have on the time taken for 500 C to pass the point?

2 Calculate the total resistance R of the arrangements below.

a)

8 Ω

10 Ω

b)

80 Ω   60 Ω

30 Ω

c)

18 Ω   10 Ω   12 Ω   2.0 Ω

4.0 Ω   7.0 Ω

3 A cell has an EMF of 12 V and an internal resistance of 3 Ω. When placed in a circuit with a lamp, a current of 2 A is drawn from the cell. Calculate the output PD of the cell.

4 Calculate resistance R.

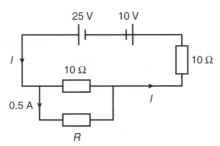

25 V   10 V

I

10 Ω

10 Ω

0.5 A

R

I

Answers

If you got them all right, skip to page 28

25

DC circuits

Improve your knowledge

25 minutes

1 **Current** (symbol *I*, unit amperes A) is a **flow of charged particles**. In metals these are electrons.

- **Current is the number of coulombs of charge (*Q*) passing a point in a circuit every second**.

$$I = \frac{Q}{t}$$

- **A potential difference** PD (symbol *V*, unit volts V) will result in **charge flow**. Charge will flow between two points only if they are at **different potentials**.
- **The potential difference between two points is the amount of electrical energy (*W*) converted into other forms per coulomb of charge passing between the points**.

$$V = \frac{W}{Q}$$

- **Ohm's Law** describes the relationship between current and voltage.
- **The current through a conductor is proportional to the potential difference across its ends provided the temperature remains constant**.

$V \propto I$
$V = IR$
where *R* = resistance, unit ohms Ω.

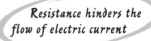

Resistance hinders the flow of electric current

2 Two resistors arranged in **series** will have a **greater total resistance R** than the same resistors arranged in **parallel**.

- In series: $R = R_1 + R_2$
- In parallel: $\frac{1}{R} = \frac{1}{R_1} + \frac{1}{R_2}$

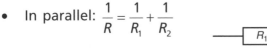

Series

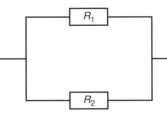

Parallel

3 If the potential difference across the terminals (terminal PD) of an isolated cell is measured, it has its maximum value and is called the **EMF (electromotive force)**. It is this EMF(E) that drives current around a circuit.

- When a current is drawn from the cell, the cell itself has a resistance. This is called the **internal resistance** of the cell. Some of the EMF has to overcome this resistance, resulting in a lower output PD for the circuit components.

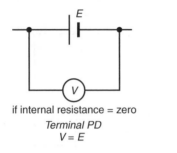

if internal resistance = zero
Terminal PD
$V = E$

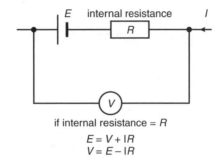

if internal resistance = R
$E = V + IR$
$V = E - IR$

4 **Kirchoff's Laws** are used in DC circuit problems:

- First Law: **The total current into a circuit junction is equal to the total current out of the junction**.
- Second Law: **For any path in a circuit which forms a complete loop, the sum of the EMFs equals the sum of the products of current and resistance (allowing for polarity)**.

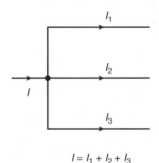

$I = I_1 + I_2 + I_3$

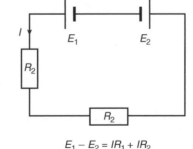

$E_1 - E_2 = IR_1 + IR_2$

DC circuits

Use your knowledge

30
minutes

Hints

1 If the cell in the circuit below has zero internal resistance, calculate:

a) The current leaving the cell.

b) How much charge passes through the 8 Ω resistor in 20 s?

2 V

8 Ω

4 Ω

2 Ω

Calculate the total of the 4 Ω and 2 Ω parallel arrangement, and add to the 8 Ω resistance. Use Ohm's Law to find I

2 For the circuit below, calculate:

a) The current in the 40 Ω resistor.
b) The current in the 80 Ω resistor.
c) The current in the 20 Ω resistor.
d) The current leaving the cell.

20 V

I

I

80 Ω

20 Ω

40 Ω

Find the current drawn from the cell, as above. Then use Kirchoff's Laws

3 A cell with an EMF of 12 V and an internal resistance 2 Ω is connected across a lamp of resistance 46 Ω. Calculate the terminal PD when the lamp is glowing.

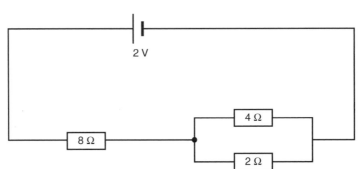

$E = 2\,V$

R

2 Ω

I

I

V

Use
$V = E - IR$

✓ *Answers on page 73*

Alternating current

30 minutes

Test your knowledge

1. a) Calculate the RMS voltage of an AC supply of peak value 100 V.
    b) If the supply has a frequency of 50 Hz determine the magnitude of the voltage 0.008 s following a zero voltage.

2. If the RMS current in a circuit is 1.5 A provided by a 20V peak supply, determine the impedance of the circuit.

3. Calculate the inductive reactance of a 0.8 H inductor connected to a 100 Hz AC supply.

4. The capacitive reactance of a capacitor connected to an AC supply is measured to be X_c. Determine, in terms of X_c, the new capacitive reactance if the capacitance and supply frequency is doubled.

5. Determine the total impedance for a 100 Ω resistor, a 2 H inductor, and a 50 μF capacitor connected in series with a 30 Hz AC supply.

6. Determine the power dissipated in the circuit described above, if connected to a 50 V RMS AC supply.

Answers

If you got them all right, skip to page 32

Answers 1 a) 70.7 V b) 58.8 V **2** 9.4 Ω **3** 503 Ω **4** $X_c/4$ **5** 289 Ω **6** 3 W

Alternating current

Improve your knowledge

35 minutes

1 The voltage of an AC power supply has a polarity that repetitively reverses in a sinusoidal manner.

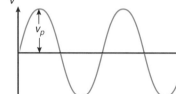

Calculator in rad mode

- The variation of voltage with time is represented by:

  $$V = V_p \sin\omega t$$

  where

  $$\omega = 2\pi f$$

- When determining the effects of AC voltages, **root mean square (RMS)** values are often used:

  $$V_{RMS} = \frac{V_p}{\sqrt{2}} \qquad I_{RMS} = \frac{I_p}{\sqrt{2}}$$

V_p = peak voltage
ω = angular frequency
t = time
f = frequency of supply

2 The total resistance of a circuit to AC is called **impedance (Z)**. The unit of impedance is the ohm (Ω).

$$Z = \frac{V_{rms}}{I_{rms}}$$

Resistors, capacitors and inductors can contribute to the total impedance.

If the circuit contains only resistor, Z = R

3 If an AC supply is connected across an inductor (coil), a back EMF is induced, resulting in a hindrance to current. This resistance to AC is called **inductive reactance X_L**.

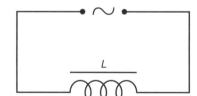

- The greater the frequency the greater the inductive reactance:

  $$X_L = \omega L = 2\pi f L$$

  where L = inductance (H).

4 When an AC supply is connected across a capacitor, the resistance to the current is greater the smaller the capacitance. The resistance due to a capacitor is known as **capacitive reactance X_c**.

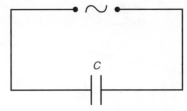

$$X_c = \frac{1}{\omega C} = \frac{1}{2\pi f C}$$

5

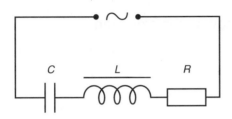

A circuit containing a series arrangement of a **capacitor, inductor and a resistor** is known as an **LCR** circuit.

- The total reactance (impedance) is given by:

$$Z^2 = R^2 + \left(\omega L - \frac{1}{\omega C}\right)^2$$

- If $\omega L = \frac{1}{\omega C}$ the current in the circuit is at a maximum.

  Resonance is said to occur at maximum current.

6 Alternating current causes heating of resistive components only. This means power is dissipated, where

$$P = I_{RMS}{}^2 R = \frac{I^2 R}{2}$$

or

$$\text{Average power} = \frac{1}{2}I^2 R$$

Alternating current

Use your knowledge

Hints

1   The voltage of an AC supply varies as shown in the diagram.

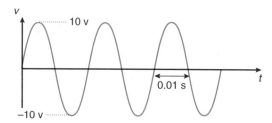

a) Determine the frequency of the supply.
b) Calculate the angular frequency of the supply.
c) State the peak voltage value.
d) How long after $t = 0$ is the voltage first equal to 2.5 V?

$T = 0.02 s$
$\omega = 2\pi f$

$V = V_p \sin\omega t$
$\omega t = \sin^{-1}(V/V_p)$

2

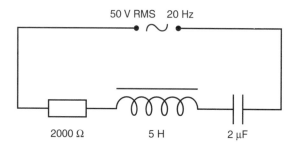

50 V RMS   20 Hz

2000 Ω   5 H   2 μF

a) Calculate the impedance of the circuit.
b) Determine I_{RMS}.
c) At which supply frequency value would the current have its
    maximum possible value?
d) Determine the RMS value of this maximum current.
e) If the power dissipated at the original frequency is P and the power
    at the maximum current frequency is P_1, determine the ratio P_1/P.

$2\pi fL = \dfrac{1}{2\pi fC}$

$\dfrac{P_1}{P} = \dfrac{I_{1RMS}^2 R}{I_{RMS}^2 R}$

Answers on page 73

Electrostatics

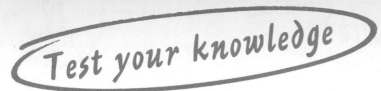

30 minutes

1 A _____ body will have a force exerted upon it if placed in an _____ field.

2 Calculate the magnitude of the force between the charged particles.

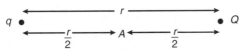

$q = 2.4 \times 10^{-17}$ C
$Q = 4.8 \times 10^{-17}$ C
$r = 2.0 \times 10^{-11}$ m
$\varepsilon_0 = 8.85 \times 10^{-12}$ Fm^{-1}

3 What would be the magnitude and direction of the electric field strength, at point A in the above example?

4 a) The definition of electrical potential involves:
   i)   Which type of charge?
   ii) Which energy term?
   iii) A reference point at zero potential by definition. Where is it?
   b) What would be the value of the electrical potential at point A in Question 2?

5 If the charges have a potential energy of 5.5×10^{-8} J, determine r.

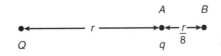

$q = 4.5 \times 10^{-9}$ C
$Q = 8.2 \times 10^{-9}$ C
$\varepsilon_0 = 8.85 \times 10^{-12}$ Fm^{-1}

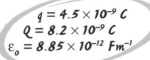

6 How much work is done in moving q from A to B in the above example?

7 a) At which point is the field strength the greatest?
   b) What is the geometrical relationship between field lines and equipotentials?

Answers

7 a) A b) They are perpendicular to each other
Answers 1 Charged/electric **2** 0.026 N **3** 2.2×10^{15} NC^{-1} **4** a) i) Unit positive ii) Work done iii) Infinity b) 65 kV **5** 6.0 m **6** -6.1×10^{-9} J

If you got them all right, skip to page 36

33

Electrostatics

Improve your knowledge

1 An **electric field** is a region within which a **charged body** will experience a **force**.

The **direction of the field** is the direction in which a small **positive charge** would be forced to **move** if positioned within the field.

2 Two charged particles will exert equal and opposite forces upon each other, since each charge is within the electric field of the other.

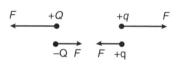

The **magnitude** of the **force** is determined by **Coulomb's Law**: $F = \dfrac{1}{4\pi\varepsilon_o}\dfrac{Qq}{r^2}$

ε_0 = permittivity of free space = 8.85×10^{-12} Fm^{-1}

3 **Electric field strength** at a given point is defined as the **force** exerted on a **unit positive** (+1C) charge at that point in the field.

where $E = \dfrac{F}{q}$

i.e. E = Electric Field Strength (NC^{-1})

A field due to a point charge has an electric field strength, at a given position, that is determined by:

at point A : $Q \bullet\!\longleftarrow\!\!-r-\!\longrightarrow\!\bullet A$ $E = \dfrac{1}{4\pi\varepsilon_o}\dfrac{Q}{r^2}$

The resultant electric field strength due to more than one point charge is determined by vectorially adding the individual field strengths.

4 The electrical potential at a given point in a field is defined as;

The work done in bringing a unit positive charge from infinity to that point in the field.

- At point A: $V = \dfrac{Q}{4\pi\varepsilon_o r}$ $Q \bullet\!\longleftarrow\!\!-r-\!\longrightarrow\!\bullet A$

- The total potential at a given point in a field, due to more than one point charge, is determined by **adding the individual potentials as scalars**.

5 The potential energy that a charge possesses at a given point in the field, is determined by multiplying the magnitude of the charge by the value of the field's electrical potential.

$Q \bullet\!\!\leftarrow\!\!\!\!-\!\!\!- r -\!\!\!-\!\!\rightarrow\!\!\bullet A$ For q at A: $PE = qV$

$$PE = \frac{qQ}{4\pi\varepsilon_o r}$$

6 The work done in moving a charge between two given points in a field is determined by subtracting the charge's initial potential energy from its final potential energy.

- If the charged particle is moved from A to B.

  Work done $= qV_B - qV_A = q(V_B - V_A)$

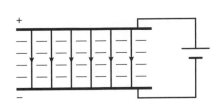

7 **Field lines** indicate the strength and direction of electric fields.

- The **strength** of the field is indicated by how close the lines are together.
- Lines joining points of the **same potential** are known as **equipotential lines**.
- Field lines and equipotentials are always **perpendicular** to each other.

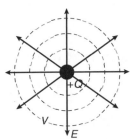

Positively-charged body

Electrostatics

Use your knowledge

30 minutes

Hints

$\varepsilon_o = 8.85 \times 10^{-12}$ Fm^{-1}
$Q = 5.0 \times 10^{-3}$ C

Use Coulomb's Law

$F \propto \dfrac{1}{r^2}$

Calculate the force exerted by each charge independently. Find the resultant

1

$+Q$ • $A \longleftarrow$ —1 m— $\longrightarrow$ • $-Q$

$\longleftarrow$ —2 m— $\longrightarrow$

a) Calculate the forces acting on the particles and indicate the directions in which they act.
b) Determine the new force if the particle separation triples.
c) Calculate the resultant force that would act upon a third particle with a charge 2 Q placed at A.

2

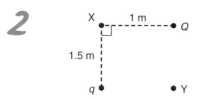

$\varepsilon_o = 8.85 \times 10^{-12}$ Fm^{-1}
$Q = 8.0 \times 10^{-5}$ C
$q = 12 \times 10^{-5}$ C

a) Calculate the magnitude of the electric field strength at X.

Find field strengths due to q and Q and add as vectors

b) Calculate the value of the potential at X.

Potentials add as scalars

c) How much work is done when a 2 μC charge is moved from X to Y?

Work done = final PE – initial PE

3 a) Calculate the values of work done if a 2 μC particle is moved along path:
i)   A.
ii) B.
iii) C.
b) Add three field lines to the diagram.

Work done = charge × (final potential – initial potential)

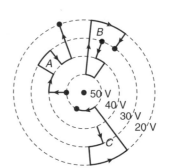

✓ Answers on page 73

Gravitation

1 All bodies are surrounded by a region called a _____ field.

Within this field all other bodies will experience an _____ force.

2 a) Calculate the force between the Earth and a 20 kg mass, where the separation of their centres is 20 000 km. ($G = 6.7 \times 10^{-11}$ Nm^{2}kg^{-2}, $m_{Earth} = 6.0 \times 10^{24}$ kg)

b) If the force acting between two identical masses is F, then calculate, in terms of F, the force acting when their separation is halved and each mass is doubled.

3 Calculate the magnitude of the gravitational field strength at A.

$r = 2 \times 10^6$ m

O⟶ A ($G = 6.7 \times 10^{-11}$ Nm^{2}kg^{-2})

$m = 1 \times 10^4$ kg

4 a) What is the defined value of gravitational potential at infinity?

b) What do all other values, at all the other locations, have in common?

c) Calculate the gravitational potential at point A in Question 3.

5 Calculate the potential energy that a 4×10^3 kg mass would have at point A in Question 3.

6 Calculate the work done moving a 20 kg body from the surface of the Earth to a point 12 800 km from the surface of the Earth.
($G = 6.7 \times 10^{-11}$ Nm^{2}kg^{-2}, $m_{Earth} = 6.0 \times 10^{24}$ kg, $r_{Earth} = 6.4 \times 10^6$ m).

7 If the dotted lines are equipotentials how do you know that the solid line is not a correct representation of the corresponding field line?

Answers

✓ *If you got them all right, skip to page 40*

37

Gravitation

30 minutes

Improve your knowledge

1 A **gravitational field** is a region within which a **mass** will **experience a force.**

Any two bodies with mass will exert attractive forces upon each other, since each mass is within the gravitational field of the other.

2 **Newton's Law of Gravitation** states the attractive force between two bodies is:

- **Proportional to the product of their masses.**
- **Inversely proportional to the square of the separation of their centres.**

$$F \propto \frac{mM}{r^2}$$

$$F = \frac{GmM}{r^2}$$ G = universal gravitational constant
$$= 6.7 \times 10^{11} \text{ Nm}^2\text{kg}^{-2}$$

Gravitational field strength at a given point is defined as **the force exerted on a unit mass (1 kg) at that point in the field:**

$$g = \frac{F}{m}$$ where g = gravitational field strength (Nkg⁻¹ or ms⁻²).

3 A field due to a spherical body has a **gravitational field strength** at a given point determined by substituting $m = 1$ kg into the force equation.

- At point A: $g = \dfrac{GM}{r^2}$

- The resultant gravitational field strength due to more than one body is determined by **vectorially adding the individual field strengths.**

4 The **gravitational potential** at a given point in a field is defined as

the work done in bringing a unit mass (1 kg) from infinity to that point in the field.

- The potential (and hence potential energy of all bodies) at infinity is defined to be zero. Work has to be done on a mass to move it towards infinity, yet at infinity it would have zero potential energy. All points other than infinity must therefore, have negative potentials.

- At point A: So $V = \dfrac{-GM}{r}$

The total potential at a given point in a field, due to more than one body, is determined by **adding the individual potentials as scalars.**

5 The **potential energy** a body possesses at a given point in a field is determined by multiplying the magnitude of the mass by the value of the field's gravitational potential.

- At point A: $PE = \dfrac{-GMm}{r}$

6 The **work done** in moving a body between two given points in a field, is determined by subtracting the body's initial potential energy from its final potential energy.

- If the body is moved from A to B:

    Work done $= mV_B - mV_A = m(V_B - V_A)$

7 Gravitational **field lines** indicate the strength and direction of the field. The **strength** of the field is indicated by how close the lines are together.

- For a spherical mass such as a planet the field lines are always **directed towards** the body, and arranged **radially.**
- Lines joining points of the **same potential** are known as **equipotential lines.**
- Field lines and equipotentials are always **perpendicular** to each other.

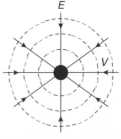

Now learn how to use your knowledge

Gravitation

Use your knowledge

35 minutes

Hints

1 Calculate the gravitational potential at the surface of the Earth.
($G = 6.7 \times 10^{-11}$ Nm²kg⁻², $m_{Earth} = 6.0 \times 10^{24}$ kg, $r_{Earth} = 6.4 \times 10^6$ m)

2 Calculate the work done moving a mass of 1000 kg along the paths indicated on the diagram below:

a) Path I.
b) Path II.
c) Path III.

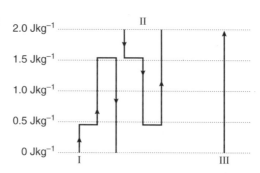

Work done = final PE − initial PE. The path followed is irrelevant. If the change in potential is zero then the work done is zero

3

Mass = x   A   Mass = x/2
$r = \sqrt{4}x$ $r = \sqrt{x}$

a) Calculate the gravitational field strength at *A* in terms of *G*.
b) Calculate, in terms of *G*, the potential energy of a body of mass $50/\sqrt{x}$ at *A*.

The xs will cancel out. The fields will be in opposite directions so subtract

4 If a human's height is in inverse proportion to the gravitational field strength of her planet, how tall would a 1.8 m Earthling be, if she were born on a planet with half the Earth's radius and twice its mass?

If $g_{Planet}/g_{Earth} = K$ then height on planet = height on Earth $\times 1/K$

✓ *Answers on page 73*

40

Current, magnetism and force

30 minutes

1 In which direction is the current in the circuit?

Explain your answer.

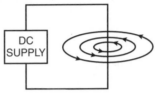

DC SUPPLY

2 a) State the factors that influence the magnitude of the magnetic flux density along the axis of a long solenoid.

b) A current causes a magnetic flux density, B, along the axis of a solenoid. Determine the magnetic flux density, in terms of B, for a solenoid with the same current flowing through it, which has the same number of turns, but is twice as long with half the diameter.

3 The wire conductor is perpendicular to a field of magnetic flux density 0.25 T. The current is 2 A.

a) Calculate the magnitude of the force on the wire.

b) Determine the direction in which the wire would move.

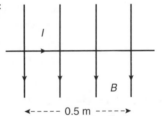

4 The two wires in the diagram would _____ each other, since each wire is in the _____ of the other. The magnitude of this force is _____ N. ($\mu_0 = 4\pi \times 10^{-7}$ Hm^{-1})

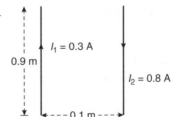

$I_1 = 0.3$ A

0.9 m

$I_2 = 0.8$ A

0.1 m

Answers

If you got them all right, skip to page 44

Improve your knowledge

1 Whenever charged particles move, they create a magnetic field around themselves. Therefore a **current carrying conductor will produce a magnetic field.**

- **Straight wire** To establish the direction of the field lines, grip the wire in your right hand. Your thumb should point in the direction of the current. The direction of the field lines is that in which your fingers wrap around the wire.

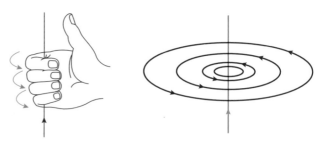

- **Solenoid** Grip the solenoid with your right hand. Fingers should be wrapped around the coil in the direction of the current. Your thumb will point to the north pole (field N to S).

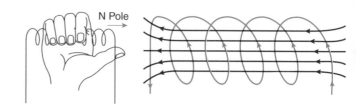

2 **Magnetic flux density (B)** indicates the **strength** and **direction** of a magnetic field. It is a vector quantity with units tesla (T).

- Long straight wire: $B = \dfrac{\mu_o I}{2\pi r}$ where μ_o = permeability of free space r = perpendicular distance to wire.

- Along the axis of a long solenoid: $B = \dfrac{\mu_o N I}{L}$ where N = number of turns L = length of solenoid.

- The middle of a flat coil: $B = \dfrac{\mu_o N I}{2r}$ where r = radius of coil.

3 If a **current-carrying conductor** is placed in a **magnetic field**, it will experience a **force.**

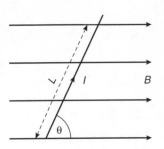

- The force is greatest when the conductor is perpendicular to the field lines.

    $F = BIL\sin\theta$

- The direction of the force is determined using **Fleming's left-hand rule:**

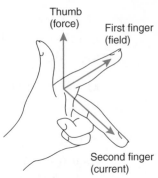

    First finger: field direction (North to South)
    Second finger: current direction
    Thumb: force direction.

- A **current-carrying coil** in a magnetic field will experience a **couple.**
  The current in the left-hand side of the coil is in the opposite direction to that in the right, so the forces on each side will be equal and opposite, resulting in a torque:

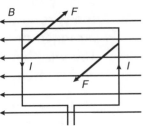

    $T = BIAn\cos\theta$
    where A = area enclosed within the coil (m²).

4 If two parallel wires carry a current, they will exert a force upon each other, as each wire is in the field of the other:

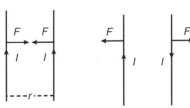

- Currents in same directions wires attract:
- Currents in opposite directions wires repel:

    $F = \dfrac{\mu_0 I_1 I_2 L}{2\pi r}$

    where r = perpendicular distance between wires.

✓ *Now learn how to use your knowledge*

Current, magnetism and force

Use your knowledge

Hints

1 The attractive force exerted on each of the parallel wires is found to be 4×10^{-7} N. ($\mu_0 = 4\pi \times 10^{-7}$ Hm^{-1})

a) Determine the direction of I.
b) Calculate the magnitude of I.

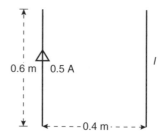

0.6 m | 0.5 A

0.4 m

Different current directions: wires repel

2 X and Y are magnets with opposite poles facing each other. The magnetic flux density in the gap is B. The length of the wire in the field is 30 cm, arranged perpendicularly to the field. The wire has an effective mass of 9 g and is in equilibrium. (g = 10 ms^{-2})

a) Determine the magnetic polarity of X and Y.
b) Calculate the magnitude of B.

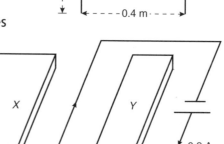

X   Y

0.3 A

Use Fleming's left-hand rule
Rearrange $F = BIL$
F must equal the weight of the wire

3 The 50-turn coil in the diagram below will rotate 0.5° for each 0.025 Nm of torque exerted upon it. The field is radial (always perpendicular to the coil). If the current in the coil is 0.2 A and the magnetic flux density is 0.5 T, then:

a) Determine in which direction the coil rotates (as viewed from above).
b) Calculate the angle through which the coil rotates.

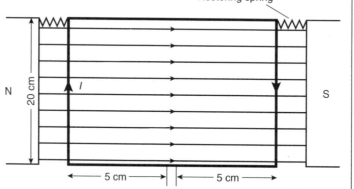

Restoring spring

N I S

20 cm

5 cm   5 cm

Use Fleming's left-hand rule either side of the coil

Divide torque by 0.025 to determine the number of 0.5° rotations

Electromagnetic induction

30 minutes

1 The horizontal metal rod moves through the vertical magnetic field at 3 ms^{-1}. 0.8 m of the conductor is in the field, which has a magnetic flux density of 0.7 T.

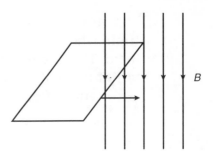

a) Calculate the EMF induced across the ends of the rod.
b) In which direction (looking from above) would the current flow in the circuit?

2 A 5-turn coil of diameter 3 cm is positioned in a magnetic field ($B = 2 \times 10^{-6}$ T). Calculate its flux linkage when the coil is:

a) Perpendicular to the field.
b) Parallel to the field.
c) Positioned with its normal at 25° to the field.

3 A square coil with 20 turns of side 5 cm is removed from a field of 2×10^{-4} T in 0.4 s.

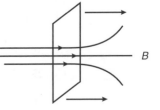

a) Determine the EMF induced in the coil.
b) Explain which pole would be induced to the left-hand side of the coil.

4 A current of 5.00 A is in a coil of 1000 turns. The current is switched off and reduces to zero in 0.4 s, inducing a back EMF of 3.75 V. Calculate the self-inductance of the coil.

5 One of a pair of coils has a current that increases at 0.5 A each second, and the other is electrically isolated. Calculate the EMF induced in the isolated coil. ($M = 0.2$ H)

Answers

4 0.3 H 5 0.1 V

that the coil is being moved away from a north pole (Lenz's Law)
c) 6.4 × 10^{-9} wb **3** a) 2.5 × 10^{-5} V b) South pole/field lines indicate
Answers 1 a) 1.7 V b) Anti-clockwise **2** a) 7.1 × 10^{-9} wb b) 0

If you got them all right, skip to page 48

Electromagnetic induction

Improve your knowledge

1 If a straight metallic conductor (wire) **is moved through** a **magnetic field**, then each electron in the metal has a force exerted on it by the field. The free electrons in the metal will move along the wire **inducing an EMF** (*E*). If the wire is connected to a complete circuit this will cause a current to flow.

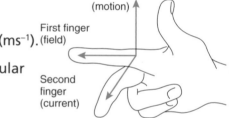

- The magnitude of the induced EMF is:

  $E = Blv$
  B = magnetic flux density, (T) [Tesla]
  l = length of conductor in field, (m)
  v = speed conductor is moved through the field (ms^{-1}).

- B is the component of flux density that is perpendicular to wire.
- The **direction** of the induced current is given by **Fleming's right-hand rule**:

2 If a coil of cross-sectional area A is placed perpendicular to a field of magnetic flux density B the **magnetic flux** ϕ (units webber (wb)) is:

  $\phi = BA$

Unit of ϕ = webber (wb)

- If the coil is at an angle to the field then:

  $\phi = BA\cos\theta$
  where θ = angle between normal to CSA and field.

- If the coil has more than one turn:
  Flux linkage = $n\phi$ where n = number of turns.

3 When the **flux linkage** in a coil **changes** an **EMF is induced**. The more rapid the change in flux linkage, the greater the induced EMF. There are two laws that describe this phenomenon:

- **Faraday's Law:** The magnitude of the induced EMF is proportional to the rate of change of flux.

- **Lenz's Law:** The direction of the current as a result of the induced EMF, always acts to oppose the change creating it.

These laws are encapsulated in the equation:

Induced EMF = – rate of change of flux linkage

$$E = -\left(\frac{\text{(final flux linkage – initial flux linkage)}}{\text{time for change}}\right)$$

so $\quad E = \dfrac{-d(n\varnothing)}{dt}$

Minus sign indicates that the induced EMF opposes the change in flux linkage

4 If there is a current in a coil, this creates a magnetic field so the coil has its own flux linkage. If the current changes this will cause a change in the flux linkage and hence an EMF will be induced. In accordance with Lenz's Law this EMF will try to oppose the change in current and is known as a **back EMF.** This effect is called **self-inductance.** The magnitude of the back EMF is:

- $E = -L\dfrac{dI}{dt}$

    where L = self inductance (H)

    $\quad dI$ = change in current

    $\quad dt$ = time for change

    $\quad \dfrac{dI}{dt}$ = rate of change of current

5 If **two coils** are close together a current flow in one will create a flux in the other. If the current in the first coil changes this will cause a change in the flux in the second coil and hence, induce an EMF. The converse of this is true: a current flowing in the second coil would induce an EMF in the first. This is known as **mutual inductance**.

- The magnitude of the induced EMF is:

    $E_2 = -M\dfrac{dI_1}{dt}$ where M = mutual inductance (H).

Electromagnetic induction

Use your knowledge

Hints

1 Two identical coils are mounted close together with a common axis. Coil A has a varying current which induces a current in coil B. Graph A plots the current magnitude in coil A against time. Sketch a corresponding current time graph for coil B. Label significant times and currents. ($M = 4 \times 10^{-4}$ H)

If coil A current is constant, induced current is zero

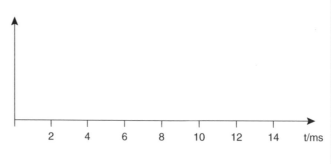

2 An aeroplane of wing span 16 m flies from the Equator towards the North Pole. The wings are perpendicular to the vertical component of the Earth's magnetic field ($B = 4 \times 10^{-5}$ T). At maximum speed, an EMF of 96 mV is induced across the wing tips. Calculate the maximum speed of the aeroplane.

Rearrange:
$E = Blv$

3 The 2000-turn coil of diameter 0.02 m is rotated from position X to position Y in 0.4 s. If the magnetic flux density is 2 T then calculate:

a) Flux linkage in position X.
b) Flux linkage in position Y.
c) The EMF induced as the coil is moved from X to Y.

X Y

$B = 2\,T$

$\phi = BA$

Flux linkage $= n\phi$

If CSA is parallel to field flux = zero

$E = - \dfrac{\partial(n\phi)}{\partial t}$

Answers on page 74

48

Capacitors

Test your knowledge

1 a) Capacitors are _____ storing devices. The more _____ they can store, per 1 V increase in PD, the greater their _____.
   b) A capacitor of capacitance 2 μF has a PD across its plates of 15 V. Calculate the charge held by the capacitor.

2 When a cell is connected across a capacitor _____ flow from the _____ terminal to one capacitor plate. _____ flow from the other plate to the _____ cell terminal.

3 Determine the energy stored in a capacitor which has a charge of 20 μC and a capacitance of 2 μF.

4 Determine the total capacitance of the arrangements shown below.

a)

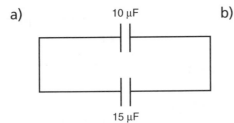

10 μF

15 μF

b)

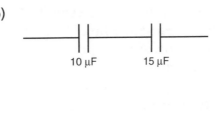

10 μF   15 μF

5 Two parallel metal plates have an overlap area of 0.05 m² and are separated by 1.5 mm. The relative permittivity of the dielectric between them is 2.5. Determine the capacitance of the arrangement.
   ($\varepsilon_0 = 8.9 \times 10^{-12}$ Fm^{-1})

6 A capacitor of 25 μF has a potential difference of 15 V across its plates. If the fully-charged capacitor is discharged through a resistor of 1×10^5 Ω, determine the PD across the capacitor after 1.5 s.

Answers

Answers 1 a) Charge/charge/capacitance b) 30 × 10⁻⁶ C
2 Electrons/negative/Electrons/positive **3** 1 × 10⁻⁴ J **4** a) 25 μF b) 6 μF
5 7.4 × 10⁻⁴ μF **6** 8.2 V

 If you got them all right, skip to page 52

Capacitors

Improve your knowledge

35 minutes

1 **Capacitors** are used to **store charge.** The **capacitance** of a capacitor is a measure of its ability to store charge.

- Capacitance is measured in farads (F). Often μF (10^{-6} F) are used.
- All capacitors consist of two parallel metal plates, which sandwich an insulator, known as a dielectric. Opposite charges are stored on the plates of the capacitor, resulting in a potential difference across the plates.

$$C = \frac{Q}{V} \quad \text{where} \quad \begin{array}{l} C = \text{capacitance (F)} \\ Q = \text{charge (C)} \\ V = \text{potential difference (V).} \end{array}$$

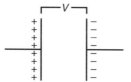

2 Connecting a cell to a capacitor results in the **flow of electrons** from the **negative terminal** of the cell to the connected **capacitor plate**. Electrons flow, at the same rate, from the opposing plate to the positive terminal of the cell, resulting in a build up of equal and opposite charges on the plates. When the capacitor is **charged** to its full capacity, **current no longer flows**. If the charged capacitor is then connected to a complete circuit the electrons will flow from the negative plate around the circuit onto the positive plate, neutralising the positive charge.

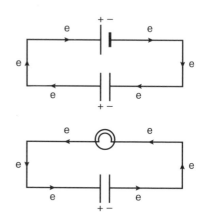

3 A charged capacitor **stores energy**, i.e. the stored charge could be used to light a flash bulb briefly.

- $E = \frac{1}{2}CV^2 = \frac{1}{2}QV$

4 The **total capacitance** of a **parallel** arrangement of capacitors is given by:

$$C = C_1 + C_2 + \text{.......}$$

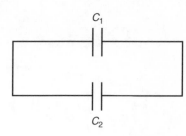

The **total capacitance** of a **series** arrangement of capacitors is:

$$\frac{1}{C_1} = \frac{1}{C_2} + \frac{1}{C_2} + \text{.......}$$

5 For a parallel-plate capacitor, the capacitance is dependent upon the plate separation, area of overlap, and the type of dielectric material:

$$C = \frac{\varepsilon A}{d} \quad \text{where} \quad \begin{aligned} A &= \text{area of overlap (m}^2\text{)} \\ d &= \text{plate of separation (m)} \\ \varepsilon &= \text{permittivity (Fm}^{-1}\text{).} \end{aligned}$$

- If the plates are separated by **air** or **vacuum** then $\varepsilon = \varepsilon_0$ where ε_0 = permittivity of free space
- Sometimes **relative permittivity** (ε_r) is stated, where $\varepsilon = \varepsilon_0 \varepsilon_r$
- So: $C = \dfrac{\varepsilon_0 \varepsilon_r A}{d}$

6 If a capacitor is **discharged** through a **resistor**:

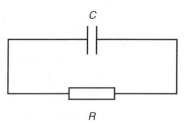

$$V = V_0 e^{-t/RC}$$
$$Q = Q_0 e^{-t/RC}$$
$$I = I_0 e^{-t/RC}$$

where V_0 = initial PD
V = PD after time t
Q_0 = initial charge on plates
Q = charge after time t
R = resistance
C = capacitance.

- RC is called the time constant (time for the charge stored on a capacitator to reduce to 30% of its original value).

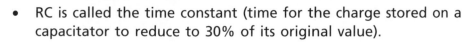

Capacitors

Use your knowledge

Hints

1. The switch is initially connected to position A, fully charging the capacitor. The capacitor is discharged through the resistor by switching to position B. Determine:

   a) The charge stored on the fully-charged capacitor.
   b) The energy stored by the fully-charged capacitor.
   c) The time constant of the discharge circuit.
   d) The PD across the plates of the capacitor 55.5 s after the switch is connected to B.
   e) The charge held by the capacitors after this time.

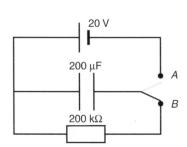

$Q = CV$

$E = \frac{1}{2} CV^2$

$V = V_0 e^{-t/RC}$

2. a) Determine the total capacitance of the network below.
   b) If the terminals of a 12 V cell are placed across A and B determine:
      i) The total charge stored on the capacitor network.
      ii) The total energy stored on the capacitor network.

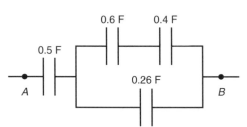

3. Two parallel metal plates are separated by an air gap d and have an area of overlap A. A potential difference V across the plates results in stored energy E. When the separation is halved and the gap is filled with a dielectric of relative permittivity 2.5, the potential difference of V results in stored energy E_1. What is the ratio E_1/E?

$C = \frac{\varepsilon_0 A}{d}$

$E = \frac{1}{2} CV^2$

Unknown values will cancel in ratio

✓ *Answers on page 74*

Basic wave properties

Test your knowledge

1 Waves transfer _____ from one place to another. There is no net _____ of the _____ that they travel through.

2 Name the two kinds of waves and state the differences between them.

3 a) For the wave in the diagram state:
    i) the amplitude.
    ii) the wavelength.
  b) If one complete wavelength takes 0.005 s to pass a point determine the frequency of the wave.

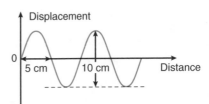

4 Determine the speed of the wave in the previous question.

5 _____ occurs when a wave moves between media of different densities. If light were to move from air to glass the ray would divert _____ the _____ line.

6 a) If water waves of wavelength λ were incident upon a gap of width d, state a condition needed for significant diffraction to occur.
  b) P and Q generate waves that are in phase. If the waves have a wavelength of 0.25 m determine the nature of the interference at X.

Answers

If you got them all right, skip to page 56

53

Improve your knowledge

25 minutes

1 **Waves transfer energy** from one place to another, without transferring any of the medium that they travel through. The particles of the medium oscillate about fixed equilibrium positions along the wave.

2 There are two kinds of waves:

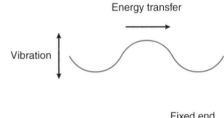

- **Transverse waves** are those that are created by **vibrations** which are **perpendicular** to the direction of energy transfer. The particles of the medium also oscillate perpendicularly to the energy transfer. Examples of transverse waves are ripples on a water surface and electromagnetic waves such as light.

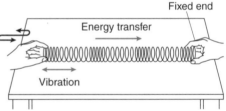

- **Longitudinal waves** are a result of **vibrations** which are **parallel** to the direction of energy transfer. The particles in the waves' medium also oscillate parallel to the energy transfer. Examples are compression waves along a spring and sound waves.

3 An understanding of the following wave terms is essential:

- **Amplitude (A)**: The maximum displacement of the particles in the wave medium from equilibrium.
- **Wavelength (λ)**: The distance between corresponding adjacent points along the wave, i.e. the distance between crests.
- **Frequency (f)**: This is the number of wavelengths passing a point each second. Units: hertz (Hz)
- **Period (T)**: This is the time for a one wavelength to pass a point.
- Period is inversely related to frequency: $T = \dfrac{1}{f}$.

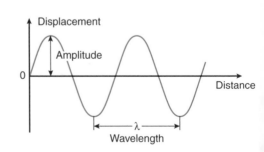

4 The **speed** of a wave is given by:
$$v = f\lambda$$

The factors that affect the speed of a wave are generally associated with the medium through which it passes:

- Waves on a string:
- Wave in a gas:

$$v = \sqrt{\frac{T}{M}}$$

$$v \propto \sqrt{\frac{P}{\rho}}$$

where T = string tension
M = mass per metre
P = gas pressure
ρ = gas density.

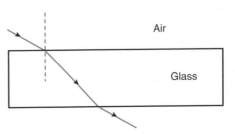

5 When a wave travels between media of differing densities it changes direction and speed. This is known as **refraction**. When light travels from low to high density it always bends towards the normal line and decreases speed and vice versa.

 6 If a wave moves through a small gap (comparable to λ) then it spreads out sideways. This is called **diffraction**. The bigger the gap the less the diffraction.

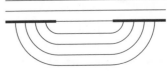

- If two waves arrive at the same point at the same time, they can pass on through the point unaffected by the rendezvous, but while at the point they combine. This is called **superposition** or **interference**.

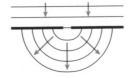

- If the waves arrive **in phase** (crests on crests) **constructive interference** will take place. If they arrive completely **out of phase** (crests on troughs) **destructive interference** occurs.

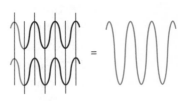

- If two waves start in phase, the difference in distances they travel to the interference point determines the type of interference. If the waves have path length L_1 and L_2:

$$L_1 - L_2 = n\lambda \text{ then constructive interference}$$
$$L_1 - L_2 = (n + 1/2)\lambda \text{ then destructive interference}$$
where n is a positive integer $0,1,2,3.\ldots$

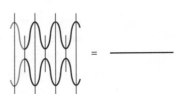

Now learn how to use your knowledge

Basic wave properties

Use your knowledge

Hints

1
a) Explain the term frequency as applied to wave motion.
b) If a wave on a plucked string has a speed *v*, determine the new speed, in terms of *v*, if the string is replaced by one of the same length, twice the mass and half the tension.

$$v = \sqrt{\frac{T}{M}}$$

2 Determine the magnitude of the gaps that would cause significant diffraction for:

a) A sound wave travelling at 330 ms⁻¹ with a frequency of 500 Hz.
b) A radio wave of speed 3×10^8 ms⁻¹ and with a frequency of 1×10^7 Hz.

Best diffraction when $d \leq \lambda$

$$\lambda = \frac{v}{f}$$

3 If the two waves are incident at the same point at the same time, sketch the result of the superposition that occurs.

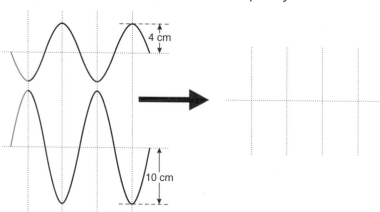

4 If *A* and *B* are the source of waves that are in phase, with $\lambda = 2$ m, determine the nature of the interference at:

a) Point *X*.
b) Point *Y*.
c) Point *Z*.

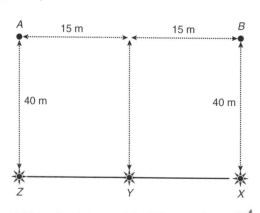

If path difference = whole number of λ then interference is constructive

✓ Answers on page 74

More on waves

25 minutes

1 The source emits sound waves, which travel at 330 ms^{-1} at 100 Hz. The frequency of the detected sound wave is found to differ from that emitted.

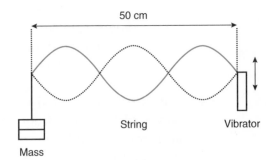

a) What is the name of the effect causing the frequency to change?
b) If the source is approaching the detector, how does the frequency detected differ from the emitted frequency?
c) By how many hertz does the frequency change?

2 a) Label the diagram with nodes and anti-nodes.
b) If the wave speed = 250 ms^{-1}, calculate the frequency for the harmonic shown in the diagram.
c) Determine the fundamental frequency.

3 A ray of light passes from air to glass and makes an angle of 50° with the interface. If $n_2 = 1.5n_1$ determine the angle of refraction.

4 Consider the Young's double slit experiment shown in the diagram.

a) Determine the separation of the observed fringes.
b) How far from the centre of the pattern is the tenth fringe?

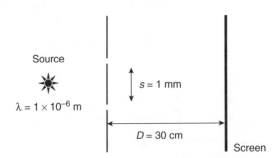

Answers

 If you got them all right, skip to page 60

57

More on waves

Improve your knowledge

1 The **Doppler effect** occurs when there is **relative motion** between a **source** of waves and an **observer**. If the relative motion results in the **distance** between the source and observer **decreasing** then: observed **frequency increases** and the observed wavelength decreases. The opposite is true for increasing separation.

- For decreasing separation: $\quad f_d = \dfrac{f_e(c+v)}{c} \qquad \lambda_d = \dfrac{\lambda_e(c-v)}{c}$

- For increasing separation: $\quad f_d = \dfrac{f_e(c-v)}{c} \qquad \lambda_d = \dfrac{\lambda_e(c+v)}{c}$

where f_d = detected frequency f_e = emitted frequency
λ_d = detected wavelength λ_e = emitted wavelength
c = wave speed v = relative velocity between wave and observer.

2 **Standing** (stationary) waves are produced when two waves of the same frequency, speed and wavelength and similar amplitude, moving in opposite directions superimpose.

- At fixed positions there will be regions of constructive interference, called **anti-nodes** and regions of destructive interference (zero amplitude), called **nodes**.

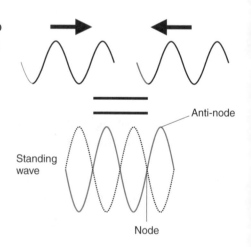

Standing wave

Anti-node

Node

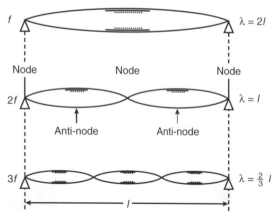

$f \qquad \lambda = 2l$

Node   Node   Node

$2f \qquad \lambda = l$

Anti-node   Anti-node

$3f \qquad \lambda = \frac{2}{3}l$

l

If a wave travels along a string that is under tension and fixed at both ends, then the reflected wave will combine with the incident wave.

- At certain frequencies superposition will result in a standing wave. The lowest frequency at which this occurs is the **fundamental frequency (f_0)**.
- Standing waves will also be formed at whole number multiples of f_0 and are called **harmonics** or **overtones**.

3 When light passes across the interface between media of differing densities it changes speed and direction. This is known as **refraction**.

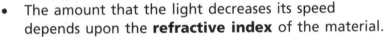

- When light passes from a less dense to a more dense medium it slows down and diverts towards the normal line.
- The amount that the light decreases its speed depends upon the **refractive index** of the material.
- **Snell's Law** states that:

$$n_1 \sin\theta_1 = n_2 \sin\theta_2$$

Also: $\dfrac{n_1}{n_2} = \dfrac{c_2}{c_1}$

where n_1 = refractive index of air, n_2 = refractive index of glass, c_1 = speed of light in air, c_2 = speed of light in glass.

4 If light passes through a slit of comparable size to its wavelength, it will **diffract**.

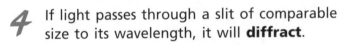

- If there are two parallel slits close together, the diffracted light from each slit will overlap and in this overlap region interference will occur.
- This phenomenon can be observed upon a screen as regions of bright and dark fringes, due to constructive and destructive interference respectively. This is known as the **Young's double slit experiment**:

$\dfrac{\lambda}{s} = \dfrac{x}{D}$ where λ = wavelength (m)
s = slit separation (m)
x = fringe separation (m)
D = perpendicular distance between slits and screen (m).

Now learn how to use your knowledge

More on waves

Use your knowledge

30 minutes

Hints

1. For the Young's double-slit experiment shown in the diagram, 30 fringes are observed between *X* and *Y*. Determine the wavelength of the light emitted by the source.

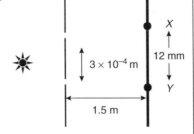

Rearrange
$$\frac{\lambda}{s} = \frac{x}{D}$$

2. For the string shown in the diagram, determine the wavelength and frequency of the three lowest-frequency standing wave modes. (Wave speed on string = 250 ms⁻¹)

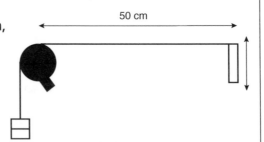

3. If the speed of light in air is 3 x 10⁸ ms⁻¹ determine the speed of the light in the glass.

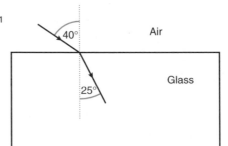

Use Snell's Law

4. A motor car and a fire engine travel towards one another at 15 ms⁻¹ and 30 ms⁻¹ respectively. The siren of the fire engine emits a sound wave of frequency 80 Hz and the speed of sound in air is 330 ms⁻¹. Determine:

a) The frequency of the sound heard by the car driver.
b) The wavelength of the wave that reaches the driver.

Answers on page 74

The nucleus

30 minutes

1 $^{238}_{92}$U represents the element uranium238. The top number is called the _____ number: it represents the number of _____ and _____ in the nucleus. The bottom number is the _____ number, representing the number of _____. All nuclei are _____ charged and contain the vast majority of the atomic _____.

2 Calculate for $^{235}_{92}$U:

a) The mass defect.
b) The binding energy.

> Masses:
> $U235 = 235.0439\ u$
> $neutron = 1.0087\ u$
> $proton = 1.00728\ u$
> $1\ u = 1.661 \times 10^{-27}\ kg$
> $c = 3 \times 10^8\ ms^{-1}$

3 Determine by calculation which is the more stable:

$^{14}_{6}$C or $^{92}_{36}$Kr

> Masses:
> $C14 = 14.003\ u$
> $Kr92 = 91.9264\ u$
> $neutron = 1.0087\ u$
> $proton = 1.00728\ u$
> $1\ u = 1.661 \times 10^{-27}\ kg$
> $c = 3 \times 10^8\ ms^{-1}$

4 a) Define nuclear fission.
b) Calculate the energy released in the fusion reaction:

$$^{2}_{1}H + ^{3}_{1}H \rightarrow ^{4}_{2}He + ^{1}_{0}n$$

5 Express 1 kg as:

a) Atomic mass units (u).
b) Electron volts (eV).

> Masses:
> $H2 = 2.014102\ u$
> $H3 = 3.016049\ u$
> $He4 = 4.002604\ u$
> $neutron = 1.0087\ u$
> $1\ u = 1.661 \times 10^{-27}\ kg$
> $c = 3 \times 10^8\ ms^{-1}$

 If you got them all right, skip to page 64

The nucleus

Improve your knowledge

30 minutes

1 At the **centre** of every **atom** is a **nucleus**. More than 99.9% of the atomic mass is concentrated within the nucleus which has a diameter 100 000 times less than the diameter of the atom.

- Within the nucleus are **protons** and **neutrons**. Protons are positively-charged and neutrons have no charge, so overall the **nucleus** has a **positive charge**. Protons and neutrons are collectively called nucleons.
- It is the number of protons in a nucleus that gives an atom its identity. The **number** of **protons** in a nucleus is called the **proton number** (also atomic number), and **the number of protons + neutrons** is called the **nucleon number** (also mass number) i.e.

$$A \quad \text{where} \quad A = \text{nucleon number (n + p)}$$
$$\begin{array}{c} \text{Y} \\ \text{Z} \end{array} \quad\quad Z = \text{proton number (p)}$$

Atom diameter approx. 10^{-10}m
Nuclear diameter approx. 10^{-15}m

2 Einstein proposed that **mass and energy are interchangeable**, i.e. mass can become energy and energy can become mass. The two are related by the equation:

$$E = mc^2 \quad \text{where} \quad \begin{array}{l} E = \text{energy (J)} \\ m = \text{mass (kg)} \\ c = \text{speed of light } (3 \times 10^8 \text{ ms}^{-1}). \end{array}$$

- If the mass of a nucleus is compared to the combined mass of the protons and neutrons that it is made from, **the mass of the nucleus is always found to be less than the mass of the constituent protons and neutrons**. The difference in mass is called the **mass defect**:

  Mass defect = mass of nucleons – mass of nucleus

- When protons and neutrons are combined to form a nucleus, energy is released. This release of energy removes mass from the nucleus in accordance with Einstein's equation. This energy is known as the nuclear **binding energy (BE)**:

$$\text{Binding energy} = \text{mass defect} \times c^2$$

- If this amount of energy is released on creating a nucleus from its constituent nucleons, the same amount of energy has to be supplied to break up the nucleus into its constituent nucleons. Hence the name binding energy.

3 Dividing the BE of a nucleus by the nucleon number gives the **BE per nucleon**. This reveals the relative **stability** of the nucleus.

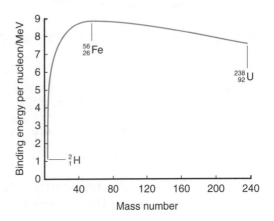

- **The greater the BE per nucleon, the more stable the nucleus** (less likely to change).
- A plot of BE/nucleon against nucleon number is shown in the diagram.
- Nuclei near the peak of the graph have the greatest BE per nucleon and are therefore the most stable. Fe is one of the most stable.

4 **Nuclear fission** occurs when a **heavy nucleus splits** into lighter nuclei with the **release of energy**. The lighter nuclei will be more stable than the original nucleus (positioned further up the peak) as they have a greater BE per nucleon.

- Fission occurs with **nuclei to the right of the peak**.

Nuclear fusion occurs when **two light nuclei join** to form a heavier more stable nucleus with the release of energy. The fusion product has a greater BE per nucleon than the original nuclei (further up the peak).

- Fusion occurs with **nuclei to the left of the peak**.

5 Units of mass and energy commonly used in nuclear problems are:

- The **atomic mass unit**: $1\ u = 1.661 \times 10^{-27}\ kg$
- The **electron volt**: $1\ eV = 1.6 \times 10^{-19}\ J$

    where $1\ u = 932\ MeV$.

The nucleus

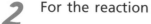

Use your knowledge

30 minutes

Hints

1 State the difference between nuclear fusion and nuclear fission.

2 For the reaction

$$^{235}_{92}U + ^{1}_{0}n \rightarrow ^{146}_{57}La + ^{87}_{35}Br + 3^{1}_{0}n$$

a) Determine by calculation which is the more stable:

La146 or Br87

b) Calculate the energy released per U235 fission.
c) Calculate the energy released when a 10 kg sample of U235 undergoes complete fission.

3 Sketch a graph with labelled axes of nucleon number against binding energy per nucleon. Indicate on your graph the positions of $^{1}_{1}H$, $^{56}_{26}Fe$, $^{238}_{92}U$. Label the regions where fission and fusion occur.

4 Look at the reaction $^{4}_{2}He + ^{1}_{0}n$ [ ] $^{2}_{1}H + ^{3}_{1}H$.

a) Place an arrow in the box to indicate the direction of the reaction.
b) Justify your answer numerically.

c) Calculate the total energy released if the reaction involves 4 kg and 6 kg of $^{2}_{1}H$ and $^{3}_{1}H$ respectively.
d) Compare your above answer to the energy released for 10 kg of U235 in Question 2 c) above.

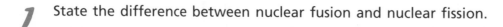

Masses:
U235 = 235.0439 u
La146 = 145.90 u
Br87 = 86.92 u
neutron = 1.0087 u
proton = 1.00728 u
1 u = 1.661 × 10⁻²⁷

c = 3 × 10⁻⁸ ms⁻¹

Multiply answer for one nucleus by the number of nuclei in 10 kg

Are the masses on both sides equal? If not why not?

Calculate the energy per fission and multiply by the number of H nuclei in 6 kg

$^{2}_{1}H$ = 3.345 × 10⁻²⁷
$^{3}_{1}H$ = 5.008 × 10⁻²⁷
$^{4}_{2}He$ = 6.647 × 10⁻²
$^{1}_{0}n$ = 1.675 × 10⁻²⁷
c = 3 × 10⁸ ms⁻¹

✓ Answers on page 74

Radioactivity

Test your knowledge

1
a) Name the three types of ionising radiation.
b) Which type of ionising radiation is emitted in the following decay?

$$^{224}_{88}\text{Ra} \rightarrow {}^{220}_{86}\text{Rn}$$

c) Determine the values of X and Y

$$^{X}_{5}\text{B} \rightarrow {}^{12}_{Y}\text{C} + \beta$$

2 List α, β, γ radiation in ascending order of:

a) Ionising ability.
b) Speed.
c) Mass.

3 Calculate the activity of a pure sample of uranium containing 2.0×10^{90} atoms, with a decay constant of 4.9×10^{-18} s^{-1}.

4 If a sample of radioactive material initially has 3.7×10^{7} unstable nuclei, how many would remain after 28 hours if the decay constant is 1.5×10^{-4} s^{-1}?

5
a) Calculate the half-life of a radioactive sample with a decay constant of 2.3×10^{-7} s^{-1}.
b) If a sample initially contains N_0 undecayed atoms, how many would remain following four half-lives?

Answers

 If you got them all right, skip to page 68

65

Radioactivity

Improve your knowledge

25 minutes

1 The **nuclei** of unstable elements **disintegrate** randomly and spontaneously into **different nuclei** of more stable elements. The disintegration (decay) can result in the emission of **ionising radiation** which consists of one or more of: **alpha** particles (α), **beta** particles (β) and less frequently **gamma** rays (γ).

- In the reactions

$$^{232}_{90}\text{Th} \rightarrow\ ^{228}_{88}\text{Ra} + ^{4}_{2}\alpha$$

$$^{14}_{6}\text{C} \rightarrow\ ^{14}_{7}\text{N} + ^{0}_{-1}\beta$$

- Top number = nucleon number (number of protons + neutrons)
- Bottom number = proton number (number of protons).
- The disintegrating nucleus is called the **parent nucleus**, the created nucleus the **daughter nucleus**.
- γ-rays carry away excess energy when a daughter nucleus is created in an excited state.

2 The **properties** of ionising radiation are summarised below:

Type	Nature	Speed	Mass/kg	Charge	Deflecting fields	Ionising ability	Distance in air	Stopped by
α	He nucleus	0.06c	6.4×10^{-27}	$+2\ e$	Magnetic Electric	Very good	Approx 5 cm	0.5 mm paper
β	Fast electron	0.98c	9.1×10^{-31}	$-1\ e$	Magnetic Electric	Good	Approx 500 cm	0.5 mm Al
γ	em radiation	c	0	0	None	Very poor	∞	Thick Pb

3 The disintegration (decay) of nuclei is a random process but the more nuclei present in a sample the greater the chance of detecting a disintegration.

- The number of **disintegrations per second** is known as the **activity** ($\frac{\partial N}{\partial t}$) of the sample:

$$\frac{dN}{dt} = -\lambda N \text{ where } \lambda = \textbf{decay constant } (s^{-1}).$$

- The minus sign indicates that N decreases with time.

4 The number of **unstable nuclei** remaining in a sample after a given time is:

$$N = N_0 e^{-\lambda t}$$

where N = number of nuclei after time t
             N_0 = number at $t = 0$

- Also:

$$I = I_0 e^{-\lambda t}$$
$$A = A_0 e^{-\lambda t}$$

where I = measured intensity
             A = activity.

5 While the underlying nature of radioactive decay is random, we can make accurate predictions about the behaviour of a sample containing a large number of atoms, such as its half-life. The **half-life** is defined as **the time taken for half the unstable nuclei of a sample to decay**.

- The half-life can be calculated using:

$$T_{\frac{1}{2}} = \frac{\ln 2}{\lambda} \qquad \text{where } \ln 2 = 0.693$$

- The **half-life** of a sample containing one kind of atom is **constant**. A plot of N against t is an **exponential decay** curve.

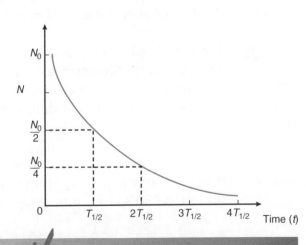

Radioactivity

Use your knowledge

Hints

1 A beam of ionising radiation known to contain alpha, beta and gamma radiation passes into a magnetic field as shown in the diagram below. Determine the nature of the beams Q and R.

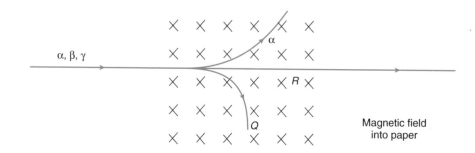

α, β, γ

Magnetic field into paper

2 The nuclei in a radioactive sample of 2.0×10^{40} polonium atoms decay according to the equation below:

$$^{218}_{X}\text{Po} \rightarrow ^{214}_{82}\text{Pb} + ^{Y}_{2}\text{Z}$$

a) Determine values of X and Y.
b) Identify the ionising radiation Z.

The total nucleon number (and proton number) must be the same on both sides of the equation.

3 The half-life of Po is 1.2×10^7 s. Determine the time elapsed when the number of remaining Po atoms falls to 1.2×10^3.

Use $N = N_0 e^{-\lambda t}$ and then take natural logarithms of both sides.

4 The measured activity of a source emitting gamma radiation is found to decrease as the detector is moved away from the source. It is established that the measured activity (A) is related to the separation between the source and detector (r) by:

$$A = \frac{1}{r^2}$$

If at $r = 2$ m the activity is measured to be 5×10^{10} s^{-1} what would the activity be 30 s later, 4 m away? ($T_{1/2} = 18$ s)

Calculate the activity at 2 m at $t = 30$ s. Doubling the separation will quarter the measured activity

Answers on page 74

Gases

Test your knowledge

1 For a 96 g sample of oxygen determine:

a) The number of moles of oxygen molecules.
b) The number of molecules.

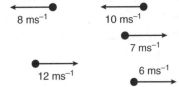

Molar mass of oxygen= 32 gmol^{-1}
$N_a = 6.02 \times 10^{23}$ mol^{-1}

2 For the molecules in the diagram determine:

a) The average velocity.
b) The mean square speed.
c) The root mean square speed.

8 ms^{-1} 10 ms^{-1}

7 ms^{-1}

12 ms^{-1} 6 ms^{-1}

3 Boyle's Law states that for a fixed _____ of gas at a constant _____ the product of _____ and _____ is _____.

4 A vessel of volume 30×10^{-2} m^3 contains gas at a pressure of 2000 Nm^{-2} at a temperature of 330 K. Calculate:

a) The number of moles of gas.
b) The number of molecules of gas.

$R = 8.31$ JK^{-1} mol
$N_a = 6.02 \times 10^{23}$ mol^{-1}

5 A 2 kg sample of gas contains molecules with a mean square speed of 2500 ms^{-1}. If the container has a volume of 2×10^{-3} m^3 determine the pressure of the gas.

6 If the temperature of a gas is doubled what effect does this have on:

a) The average KE per molecule?
b) The root mean square speed of the molecules?

Answers

Answers 1 a) 3 moles b) 9.06×10^{23} molecules **2** a) 1.4 ms^{-1} to the right b) 78.6 ms^{-1} c) 8.9 ms^{-1} **3** Mass/temperature/pressure/volume /constant **4** a) 0.22 moles b) 1.3×10^{23} molecules **5** 8.33×10^5 Nm^{-2} **6** a) Doubled b) $\times \sqrt{2}$

If you got them all right, skip to page 72

Gases

Improve your knowledge

1 An appreciation of the following terms is essential when considering gases:

- **The mole:** The amount of a substance that contains Avogadro's number of particles.
- **Avogadro's number (N_a) = 6.022 × 10²³ mol⁻¹:** The number of particles in one mole of a substance.
- **Molar mass:** The mass of one mole (6.022 × 10²³) of atoms of a substance.

2 For n molecules/atoms of a gas with speeds $c_1, c_2, c_3 \ldots c_n$:

- **Mean speed =**
$$\bar{c} = \frac{c_1 + c_2 + c_3 + \ldots c_n}{n}$$

- **Mean square speed =**
$$\bar{c}^2 = \frac{c_1^2 + c_2^2 + c_3^2 + \ldots c_n^2}{n}$$

- **Root mean square speed =**
$$\sqrt{\bar{c}^2} = \sqrt{\frac{c_1^2 + c_2^2 + c_3^2 + \ldots c_n^2}{n}}$$

3 The three laws that describe the behaviour of gases are:

- **Boyle's Law:** $P \propto \dfrac{1}{V}$ Fixed mass, constant temperature.

- **Charles' Law** $V \propto T$ Fixed mass, constant pressure.
- **Pressure Law** $P \propto T$ Fixed mass, constant volume.

$P = pressure\ (Nm^{-2})$
$V = volume\ (m^3)$
$T = temperature\ (K)$

4 An **ideal gas** is one which obeys each of the gas laws. No gas is completely ideal, but as a theoretical concept it is useful when modelling the behaviour of gases.

The following conditions are assumed to be met by an ideal gas:

- There are a large number of molecules moving randomly.
- The molecules continuously collide with each other and the walls of its container.

- The volume of the molecules is negligible compared to that of the container.
- Apart from during collision the forces between molecules are negligible.
- The contact time during a collision is negligible compared with the time spent between collisions.
- All collisions are elastic (KE conserved).

The equation which describes the behaviour of an ideal gas is called **the equation of state of an ideal gas**:

$$PV = nRT$$

or

$$PV = NkT$$

- For a particular gas this leads to:

$$\frac{P_1V_1}{T_1} = \frac{P_2V_2}{T_2}$$

where n = number of moles (mol), N = number of molecules, R = Universal Molar Gas constant (8.31 JK^{-1} mol^{-1}), k = Boltzmann's constant (1.38 $\times$ 10^{-23} JK^{-1}).

5 The **pressure** of an ideal gas is related to the mean square speed of its molecules and its density by:

$$P = \frac{1}{3}\rho\bar{c}^2 \qquad \text{where } \rho = \text{gas density (kgm}^{-3})$$

6 The **average kinetic energy** per molecule of an ideal gas is:

$$\overline{KE}_{molecule} = \frac{1}{2}m\bar{c}^2 = \frac{3}{2}kT$$

- Per mole:

$$\overline{KE}_{mole} = \frac{1}{2}M\bar{c}^2 = \frac{3}{2}RT$$

where m = mass of one molecule, M = mass of one mole.

Gases

Use your knowledge

30 minutes

Hints

1 a) Identify each symbol in the equation $PV = nRT$.
   b) A gas container of volume 1 m^3 contains a gas with a pressure of
       1.5×10^7 Nm^{-2}. If the molar mass of the gas is 32 g and its
       temperature = 27 °C determine:
       i)   The number of moles of gas in the container.

       ii) The mass of gas in the container.
       iii) If the container has a safety valve that releases gas when the
            internal pressure exceeds 30×10^5 Nm^{-2} determine the mass of
            gas released if the temperature of the container rises to 54 °C.

$R = 8.31 JK^{-1} mol^{-1}$

$n = \dfrac{PV}{RT}$

Mass = $n \times$ number of moles

2 State three conditions (other than obeying the gas laws) that an ideal
   gas has to satisfy.

3 An ideal gas at a pressure of 2×10^5 Nm^{-2} is trapped within a thermally
   isolated container of variable volume. The initial volume of the
   container is 5×10^{-2} m^3 and contains 30 g of gas at 300 K. Determine:

   a) The number of moles of gas present.
   b) The molar mass of the gas.
   c) The mean square speed of the molecules.

$R = 8.31 JK^{-1} mol^{-1}$

$P = \dfrac{1}{3}\rho \bar{c}^2$

4 A gas is held in a vessel of volume 0.01 m^3 under a pressure of 5×10^6
   Nm^{-2} at 350 °C. If the gas is released so that it is at atmospheric
   pressure (1×10^5 Nm^{-2}) and 300 °C then determine its new volume.

$\dfrac{P_1 V_1}{T_1} = \dfrac{P_2 V_2}{T_2}$.

✓ Answers on page 74

Answers to

Use your knowledge

tests

Motion

1a)i) 11.7 m ii) 1.5 m in the direction A to B iii) 6.9 ms^{-1} iv) 0.88 ms^{-1} in the direction A to B b) 367 ms^{-2}

2a) 7 ms^{-1} downward b) 10 ms^{-2} c) 4.9 m

3 750 ms^{-1}

4 Helicopter increases the downward momentum of a column of air, so a force must be exerted upon the air/Newton's Second Law. An equal and opposite force is exerted by the air on the helicopter/Newton's Third Law. If the weight of the helicopter is equal to this upward force, then no resultant force acts on the helicopter, so it can remain stationary (hover)/Newton's First Law.

Vectors

1a) 193 ms^{-1} b) 230 ms^{-1} c) 8.97 km

2a) 345 N b) Down

3a) F_2 = 269 N b) 112°

Forces

1 514 N

2a) 260 N b) 3160 N

3 1.5

4a) 48.2° b) 13.5 N

Work, energy and power

1a) 7.2 m b) 3.6 m c) 5 m

2 5 m

3a) 2 kW b) 8.3 kW c) 4 kW

4a) 5000 N b) 90 kW

Circular motion

1 0.23

2a) Towards the centre of the circle b) 10 688 N c) Friction between the tyres and the road d) 11.3 ms^{-2}

3a) 7.3 × 10^{-5} rad s^{-1} b) 465.4 ms^{-1} c) 0.0034 ms^{-2} d) Double

Simple harmonic motion

1a) 250 ms^{-2} b) 25.3 m c) 79.5 ms^{-1} d) 63.2 kJ e) 46.7 ms^{-1}

2 a)i) $\sqrt{0.02}$ k ii) 0.2 k iii) $\sqrt{0.017}$ k b)i) $\sqrt{2}$ ii) 2

DC circuits

1a) 0.2 A b) 4 C

2a) 0.35 A b) 0.07 A c) 0.28 A d) 0.35 A

3 11.5 V

Alternating current

1a) 50 Hz b) 100π Hz c) 10 V d) 8 × 10^{-4} s

2a) 3902 Ω b) I = 0.013 A c) 50.3 Hz d) 0.025 A e) 3.7

Electrostatics

1a) 5.6 × 10^4 N attractive b) 6.2 × 10^3 N c) 9 × 10^5 N

2a) 8.7 × 10^5 NC^{-1} b) 1.44 × 10^6 V c) 0.24 J

3a)i) −60 μJ ii) 0 J iii) 20 μJ b) Straight lines directed radially outward, perpendicular to the equipotentials

Gravitation

1 −6.3 × 10^7 Jkg^{-1}

2a) 0 J b) 0 J c) 2 kJ

3a) $G/4$ to the right b) 50 G

4 0.225 m

Current, magnetism and force

1a) Same direction as other wire b) 2.2 A

2a) X south Y north b) 1 T

3a) Clockwise b) 2°

Electromagnetic induction

1
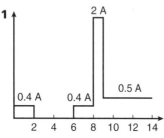

2 150 ms^{-1}

3a) 1.3 wb b) 0 c) 3.3 V

Capacitors

1a) 4×10^{-3} C b) 0.04 J c) 40 s d) 5 V e) 1×10^{-3} C

2a) 0.25 F b)i) 3 C ii) 18 J

3 $E_1/E = 5$

Basic wave properties

1a) The number of wavelengths passing a point each second b) New speed = $V/2$

2a) Approx. 0.7 m b) approx. 30 m

3
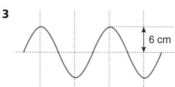
6 cm

4a) Path difference = 10 m = 5λ : constructive
b) Path difference = 0 m = 0λ : constructive c) Path difference = 10 m = 5λ : constructive

More on waves

1 8×10^{-8} m

2 λ_1 = 1m/λ_2 = 0.5m/λ_3 = 0.33m/f_1 = 250 Hz/f_2 = 500 Hz/f_3 = 750 Hz

3 2×10^8 ms^{-1}

4a) 91 Hz b) 3.6 m

The nucleus

1 Nuclear fusion is the joining of two light nuclei to form heavier, more stable nuclei. Nuclear fission is the splitting of a heavier nucleus, into lighter, more stable nuclei.

2a) Br has greater BE/nucleon (just) b) 3.1×10^{-11} J c) 7.9×10^{-14} J

3 See diagram on page 63. To the right of Fe56 fission/to the left of Fe56 fusion

4a) Right to left b) Mass of LHS is greater than mass of RHS therefore reaction occurs from right to left, losing mass as energy c) 3.3×10^{15} J d) More energy per 10 kg than for U235. Current technology does not allow for efficient harnessing of the hydrogen fusion energy

Radioactivity

1 $Q = \beta$ $R = \gamma$

2a) $X = 84$, $Y = 4$ b) Alpha particle

3 1.5×10^9 s

4 3.9×10^9 s^{-1}

Gases

1a) P = pressure (Nm^{-2}) V = volume (m^3) n = number of moles R = universal molar gas constant (8.31 JK^{-1} mol^{-1}) T = temperature (K) b)i) 6017 moles ii) 193 kg iii) Releases 157 kg

2 See page 70–1

3a) 4 moles b) 7.5 gmol^{-1} c) 1×10^6 m^{2}s^{-2}

4 0.46 m^3

Formulae and equations

page	
35	$PE = \dfrac{qQ}{4\pi\varepsilon_o r}$
38	$F = \dfrac{GmM}{r^2}$
38	$g = F/m$
38	$g = \dfrac{GM}{r^2}$
38	$F = mv^2/r$
39	$V = \dfrac{-GM}{r^2}$
39	$PE = \dfrac{-GmM}{r}$
42	$B = \dfrac{\mu_0 I}{2\pi r}$
42	$B = \dfrac{\mu_0 NI}{L}$
42	$B = \dfrac{\mu_0 NI}{2\pi}$
43	$F = BIL\sin\theta$
43	$T = BIAn\cos\theta$
43	$F = \dfrac{\mu_0 I_1 I_2 L}{2\pi r}$
46	$E = Blv$
46	$\phi = BA\cos\theta$
47	$E = \dfrac{-d(n\phi)}{dt}$
47	$E = -L\dfrac{dI}{dt}$
47	$E_2 = -M\dfrac{dI_1}{dt}$
50	$C = Q/V$
50	$E = \dfrac{1}{2}CV^2 = \dfrac{1}{2}QV$

51	$C = \dfrac{\varepsilon A}{d}$
51	$V = V_0 e^{-t/RC}$
51	$I = I_0 e^{-t/RC}$
51	$Q = Q_0 e^{-t/RC}$
55	$v = f\lambda$
58	$f_d = \dfrac{f_e(c+v)}{c}$
58	$\lambda_d = \dfrac{\lambda_e(c+v)}{c}$
59	$n_1\sin\theta_1 = n_2\sin\theta_2$
59	$n_1/n_2 = c_2/c_1$
59	$\dfrac{\lambda}{s} = \dfrac{x}{D}$
62	$E = mc^2$
67	$\dfrac{dN}{dt} = -\lambda N$
67	$N = N_0 e^{-\lambda t}$
67	$I = I_0 e^{-\lambda t}$
67	$A = A_0 e^{-\lambda t}$
67	$T_{1/2} = \ln 2/\lambda$
70	$P \propto 1/V$
70	$V \propto T$
70	$P \propto T$
71	$PV = nRT$
71	$\dfrac{P_1 V_1}{T_1} = \dfrac{P_2 V_2}{T_2}$
71	$P = \dfrac{1}{3}\rho\bar{c}^2$
71	$\overline{KE} = \dfrac{1}{2}m\bar{c}^2 = \dfrac{3}{2}kT$